INSECTS
ARE ANIMALS, TOO

Anthony Wootton

Drawings by the Author

DAVID & CHARLES
NEWTON ABBOT   LONDON   NORTH POMFRET (VT)   VANCOUVER

British Library Cataloguing in Publication Data

Wootton, Anthony
   Insects are animals, too
   1. Insects
   I. Title
   595.7   QL463

   ISBN 0–7153–7534–2

Library of Congress Catalog Card Number: 77–91775

Printed in Great Britain
by Biddles Limited, Guildford, Surrey
for David & Charles (Publishers) Limited
Brunel House Newton Abbot Devon

Published in the United States of America
by David & Charles Inc
North Pomfret Vermont 05053 USA

Published in Canada
by Douglas David & Charles Limited
1875 Welch Street North Vancouver BC

CONTENTS

1

INSECTS ARE ANIMALS, TOO

Ever since childhood I have been totally captivated by the world of insects, almost if not quite to the exclusion of other animals. It was not just the colourful butterflies and moths that attracted my interest. The myriads of other insects which vastly outnumber them but are rather more elusive also frequently appealed to a youthful delight in the *outré*. Butterflies might be absent, but there was always something to see, something new to marvel at, even in the colder months. There were species with brilliant iridescent or metallic colours, strange shapes and appendages, insects which looked like twigs or bark, leaves, or even bird droppings! Others stirred my imagination, like the delicate snake-fly which seemed to be deliberately aping the appearance of a cobra about to strike, flies and beetles resembling bees or wasps, and the tiny *Malachius* beetle which when too freely handled astonishingly extrudes brilliant scarlet bladders, their exact purpose unknown. And I marvelled at the paradox presented by species like the glow-worm, whose intensely bright greenish 'fire' never fails to excite wonder and admiration, and is in such complete contrast to the drabness of the light-producer itself.

What puzzled me as a boy, and still does today, was why more people did not share my enthusiasm. The non-entomologist was quite prepared to admire the obvious attractiveness of a gaudy Red Admiral butterfly or Garden Tiger moth, but mostly we parted company when it came to recognising the equal fascination of their

7

Two views of Bee-fly (*Bombylius major*). An example of a true fly imitating a bee (Batesian mimicry). About actual size.

wriggly, hairy, many-legged caterpillars. Somehow, they found it difficult to link the two, apparently dismissing my regard for such 'creepy-crawlies' as an illogical childish whim. I, on the other hand, marvelled at the unique nature of insects which pass through a complicated life cycle, or *metamorphosis,* so different from mammals like us, each stage of which holds equal interest and may, by judicious seeking, be found in countryside and garden.

Insect groups, like butterflies, often large and colourful, with an extrovert tendency to spread lovely wings over bright flowers, allow admiration without requiring any effort on the part of the observer. But to confine yourself to this level is to miss a whole world of other more subtle insect delights. After all, butterflies are far from numerous in this country. Only about 70 species are regarded as British, and many of these are rare or of uncertain appearance; moreover, to appreciate them only as adults is to see only part of their lives. Compare this with the total number of insects on the British list – upwards of 20,500 – and the force of the argument becomes immediately apparent. The world figure for butterflies is more impressive, of course, but still represents a mere fraction of the number of insects as a whole. No one knows for sure just how many species of insects there are throughout the world: estimates vary from around 800,000 to more than a million, and most entomologists think it possible that as many more await discovery and classification. This may seem incredible, but then insects have only relatively recently begun to attract worldwide

8

study; also many of them are small, easily overlooked and difficult to distinguish from each other.

Their creepy elusiveness, small size and alien cold-blooded nature are probably among the foremost reasons why the majority of insects do not attract the enthusiastic amateur following that, say, wild birds do, despite the fact that the ornithologist has far fewer species to study or observe. Another is probably linked to the widespread notion that apart from a few favoured individuals most insects are pests or at least a bit of a nuisance. It is unfortunate that some of the insects most likely to come to the uninitiated's notice are just those that sting or bite, or frighten the nervous by inveigling their way into the bath or whizzing around the lightshade. Most of all, the non-entomologist complains, they demonstrate a marked tendency to gobble up our crops.

Part of this pest image – palpably false as regards insects as a whole – results from one basic insect character: their ability to reproduce themselves rapidly and in great numbers when conditions are suitable. A particularly spectacular example of this is afforded by the migratory desert locust, a single swarm of which may comprise many millions, increasing daily, and do untold damage to food crops, notably in Africa and Asia. Even in Britain, large acreages of root crops and brassicas may be visited by hordes of wireworms, leatherjackets and cabbage white butterflies. Insects like these present a problem, of course, but in fact they are merely taking advantage of what is a highly unnatural if, to them, welcome situation. After all, they would never find such a concentration of their favourite pabulum in free nature. It is rather like taking a starving man to a banquet and then blaming him for eating it! Having effectively turned them into pests by concentrating their feeding and stimulating their breeding, we then resort to crop-spraying which frequently has the effect of killing the useful insects, like ichneumon flies, as well as other natural predators, including birds.

This is not intended as a total indictment of man nor as an entomologist's biased championing of the insect world. Man must live and support himself, and measures of insect control have to be taken. We can, though, cultivate a more balanced view of the Class Insecta as a whole, not just a few favoured groups. We need to recognise that the needs of insects, as of most wild animals, tend to clash with our own from time to time, but that their actions are not born of malevolence and that in any case such a conflict of interests is untypical of the tribe as a whole. Indeed, comparatively few insects are troublesome to man at all, even in the highly unnatural environment he commonly creates. Many on the contrary are distinctly helpful. We have only to think of pollinating bees, aphis-eating ladybirds, hover-flies and lacewings, the armies of predatory and waste-consuming beetles, plus a whole host of others working away unseen by the human eye to realise the truth of this.

Insects are an essential part of that natural balance which allows animals and plants to live in harmony without one species taking too great an advantage of another. They are vital link-men. Without insects not only would many of the gardener's fruits and vegetables fail, but the botanist would have far fewer wild plants to enthuse about and the ornithologist's tick-list would lack many of the insectivorous species.

But all this is as if we were offering excuses for insects' existence; as if we were trying to answer that common and highly irritating question 'What *use* are they?' There is no need for such defensiveness. Insects are not merely mostly innocuous or even useful members of the animal kingdom, but well worthy of close attention in their own right. There is more scope in entomology than in any other branch of natural history study. The unique nature of the insect

A pair of mating Southern Aeshna dragonflies (*Aeshna cyanea*). The male, above, is grasping the female by the neck while the latter brings her genital aperture into contact with a sperm-charged segment of the male's abdomen (previously filled by the male curving his abdomen forward). This curious mating procedure, which often takes place in flight when the pair are said to be 'in tandem', is unique to dragonflies. This is a common species in the south of England. Enlarged. (*G. E. Hyde*)

life cycle means that there are a whole host of pre-adult forms, many displaying little or no resemblance to their parents, and thus in effect swelling their numbers several-fold. To some people this vast assemblage of species and forms, with the difficulties of identification, may seem a bit of a deterrent. To others it is a positive challenge, not least in that surprisingly little is known about many species, even in Britain. There is always the possibility of the amateur discovering something new, particularly concerning insect behaviour, life histories and distribution. Even if he does not add to scientific knowledge, the student will learn something new to himself. From the purely aesthetic viewpoint, insects add a new dimension to nature, with their delightful diversity of colours, shapes and sizes, and variations of structure, all of them geared in the most marvellous ways to adaptation to habitat and survival.

People often maintain, perhaps without thinking, that they love animals. If this is taken literally, then insects should find equal favour, for they are very much animals too and, more to the point, certainly as interesting as any other. Yet for various reasons, insects are usually afforded scant consideration when conservation projects are mooted. When areas are set aside as nature reserves or conservation areas, the resident insects often benefit happily too; but many attractive species of insects have special habitat needs which are steadily and unthinkingly being eroded away by man. To give just one example, the tendency to clear away dead tree stumps has meant that our largest native beetle, the great Stag, is now much less common than it was, since its long-developing larvae feed solely on decaying wood. A similar story can be told of many other species, and this is to say nothing of the widespread and often indiscriminate use of insecticides and herbicides, and activities like hedge removal, pond and ditch drainage, which remove the living conditions needed by our interesting insect population. Perhaps one of the answers here is for insect enthusiasts to try to provide a variety of suitable habitats in their own gardens: trees, shrubs and flowers, ponds for aquatic species, and so on.

Before attempting this sort of thing, however, it is necessary to

Pupa of male Stag beetle (*Lucanus cervus*), showing its embryo stag-like horns, in its cell of wood-shavings. Actual size of pupa almost 2 inches. The species appears to be getting increasingly local due to a diminution of its larval food—dead and dying trees and tree stumps, notably oak. The species is protected in Germany, as it should be in Britain.

(Ray Palmer)

learn something of insects' ways, to look beyond the obvious and get down to their level in an eminently practical sense; get to know them in all their stages, in their natural and less natural habitats, exercising all of our senses whilst doing so. Above all, we need to try to cultivate a deeper understanding and appreciation of them as living sensate animals with a right to live and a deep fascination and charm all their own. This, I hope, is what my book will encourage.

2

GETTING DOWN
TO THEIR LEVEL

It is worth cultivating something of a Tom Thumb approach when looking for and at insects. Theirs is a miniature world and to study it properly we must scale down our sphere of vision so as to notice things that others, even other naturalists, would probably overlook.

Most insects are both small and adept at concealing themselves in various ways, or in making their rapid escape if disturbed: factors which enable them to survive in a wide variety of habitats.

The very largest insects of all are stick-insects some twelve inches long (although they are very thin-bodied), high-flying bird-wing butterflies seven or eight inches across the wings, or certain beetles like the weighty goliaths of tropical Africa. But, like the Death's Head hawk-moth (five inches in wing-span) or the Stag beetle (three inches long), which are the bulkiest British insects, such relative giants are exceptions to the rule. Most insects are much smaller than that, and for certain very good reasons. An over-large insect is liable to become sluggish and slow-moving, an obvious disadvantage in this 'kill or be killed' world.

Mammals and birds overcome the problem of their comparative bulk because their blood circulates air quickly and effectively to each part of the body and energises it; they can also raise their body temperature if it is cold, or cool it down (by panting or sweating) if it is too hot. Insects, by and large, can do none of these things. Unable to regulate their body temperature to any great

15

Death's Head Hawk-moth (*Acherontia atropos*). About actual size.

extent, they are active in warm weather, but become sluggish when it is cold. They breathe not through the blood (which is used solely for carrying food and waste materials), but by simple diffusion through a series of *spiracles*, or air-holes, along the sides of the body. Diffusion is a slow and relatively inefficient process and only works properly over short distances; so the longer the air-tubes, and the more ramifications they have, the longer it takes for each limb to respond to messages from the brain and move in unison.

While insects have an incredibly long evolutionary history,

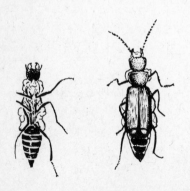

Two views of a Red-tipped Flower beetle (*Malachius bipustulatus*), showing inflated bladders, scarlet in colour, perhaps for deterring birds. Enlarged × 2 approx.

16

stretching back some 400 million years, very large ones have never lasted more than a short period of time, geologically speaking. The huge dragonflies, over two feet across the wings, which zoomed over the waters of southern England during the Carboniferous period (about 300 million years ago) were not a blueprint for later models, for their present-day descendants are a mere fraction of that size.

Within the limitations set by their physiology, however, insects are and have long been remarkably successful as a group. They are so numerous and diverse that no one entomologist, however experienced, can hope to be fully familiar even with those of his own country. In Britain alone, for example, some 20,500 or so

Third instar caterpillar of a Puss moth (*Cerura vinula*), about to change its skin while anchored to a silken pad. Enlarged.

species are known to occur. Another difficulty is that an insect may be found in any one of several distinct stages in its development, each usually markedly different from the other; it therefore presents problems of identification if the available reference books illustrate and describe only the adult stage. Unlike mammals and birds, which grow larger by increasing their body cells, most insects pass through a complicated life history involving radical changes of structure, only one stage of which is directly concerned with feeding and growing. Externally laid eggs, which themselves

17

vary considerably in size, shape and colour, hatch into larvae which may have several more legs than the adult insect—or sometimes (as in flies) none at all—and spend all their time feeding and, at intervals, changing their skin (a process called *ecdysis*). Regular skin, or cuticle, changing is necessary in insects, since the outer cuticle consists of non-living, and therefore non-growing, cells; development can continue properly only if a new and relatively elastic skin is produced beneath it. Growth ceases entirely when insects reach their final, adult stage.

There are, however, refinements and modifications of this scheme of life. In some groups, such as the bugs, crickets and grasshoppers, and dragonflies, the fully developed adult emerges directly from the full-grown larva (or nymph). In others, for example the

Larva of a Cardinal beetle (*Pyrochroa sp.*) commonly found under old tree bark. About actual size.

familiar butterflies and moths, a further pupal or chrysalid stage occurs, during which the insect is almost totally inactive. In both cases, the larval tissue is broken down and rearranged to form the adult, which eventually breaks through the nymphal or pupal husk to begin the cycle all over again by mating and egg-laying. The whole life history is called a *metamorphosis* (from the Greek 'change of form'), or for insects which have no pupation stage an *incomplete metamorphosis*.

To add a further complication, a few primitive insects (such as silverfish) scarcely change their form at all after hatching from the egg, except to grow larger after each successive moult. Some insects even produce fully formed young, near miniatures of themselves—and what is even more remarkable they do so without mating! This strange, sexless reproduction is called *parthenogenesis* (Greek *parthenos*, virgin; *genesis*, origin or birth), and is found in many other animal groups too.

Before going further, we should be clear about what an insect really is—or conversely, which creatures are really insects. Many small invertebrate animals, such as centipedes, woodlice and spiders,

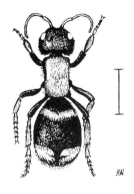

The wingless female Velvet ant (*Mutilla differens*), a non-British species, which is, however, closely related to the two British Mutillids, *M. europaea* and *M. rufipes*. Mutillids are wasps, parasitizing the nests of other Hymenoptera. Greatly enlarged.

look so like insects to most people that it sounds irritatingly pedantic to say they are not really insects at all. Although these creatures share certain characteristics with insects, they also display certain essential differences.

To begin with, all insects, centipedes, millipedes, woodlice and arachnids (spiders and related groups) belong to one great *Phylum*, or super-class, called *Arthropoda*. The term literally means 'jointed limbs' and these features, together with a hard outer chitin-strengthened 'skeleton' and a segmented body, are shared by all arthropods. It is when we look at them more closely that the differences between insects and the other arthropods appear, thus justifying their separation into different *classes*. It is not necessary to pick them up to see that centipedes and millipedes have a great many pairs of legs, spiders and their allies (such as harvestmen) a total of eight; woodlice have seven pairs, although these may be partly hidden under their overlapping carapace. By contrast, no insects possess more than six true legs in the adult stage. In their juvenile forms, such as caterpillars, some frequently have many more. But at least a spider, a centipede, a millipede or a woodlouse looks much the same whether it is adult or juvenile, because these arthropods do not undergo a metamorphosis as insects do.

In addition, insects are the only arthropods to possess wings. Not all groups or species can fly, while even those with wings may lose them after their purpose has been served; male and queen ants, for instance, discard their wings after mating, when they are of no further use. Nevertheless, it is useful to remember that any flying invertebrate animal must, *ipso facto*, be an insect. With the exception of the mayflies, pre-adult insects are totally wingless.

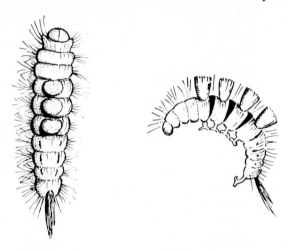

Two views of caterpillar of a Pale Tussock moth (*Dasychira pudibunda*). Above view enlarged × 1½ approx.; side view almost actual size.

What are the more promising and accessible habitats for insects? Their choice of food and shelter is practically limitless, so this brief survey can only give a general outline. Many, perhaps most, insects are herbivorous, so certain species of plants provide particularly good hunting grounds for the observant entomologist. Some kinds of trees harbour such a wealth of insect life that it is a wonder they survive under such concerted bombardment. The best example of all seems to be the common or pedunculate oak (*Quercus robur*). It has long been a symbol of strength and its ability to support so many organisms reflects its tolerance and durability. Scores of different insects live on its leaves, fruits, bark, heartwood and roots at various times of the year, not necessarily of course all on the same individual tree. Moth larvae are often numerous, one of the most striking being the caterpillar of the Pale Tussock (*Dasychira pudibunda*), which is usually a delightful pale green in

20

colour with thick brushes of yellowish-white hairs separated by black patches on the back and with a carmine tinted tuft at the tail end; another form is much duller and more yellow in appearance. The Pale Tussock larva is a solitary feeder, but others are communal such as the Buff Tip (*Phalera bucephala*) and Lackey (*Malacosoma neustria*). The former is dull yellow and black, and the latter has a slate-blue stripe down the centre of its body and a pair of black spots on its similarly coloured head, which thus presents a peculiarly skull-like appearance; both caterpillars are moderately hairy. Some idea of the multiple jaws at work on an oak's leaves can be obtained if one stands beneath it in early summer; often one will hear a continuous gentle patter, as of light rain. It is in fact falling frass, most of it resulting from the feeding activity of a myriad Oak Roller moth caterpillars (*Tortrix viridana*), each of which works alone within a folded section of leaf, though having the ability to suspend itself on a safety line of silk if dislodged. The adult moth is of disarming beauty with its pastel-green forewings.

Some species of butterflies have a habit, irritating to the observer, of flying about the tops of the very tallest oaks, but rather strangely only one chooses oak foliage as food for its caterpillars. The Purple Hairstreak (*Quercusia quercus*) is locally distributed, although its rather flat, vaguely slug-like larvae are always worth looking for from spring, when they emerge from overwintered eggs, until about June. Another typical denizen of oaks and other trees, but belonging to a different group and having distinctly different habits, is far more difficult to find. The tiny larva of the Green Lacewing (*Chrysopa*) is a mere five millimetres long, and much of that length is taken up with a pair of relatively huge caliper-like mandibles with which it sucks out the body fluids of its prey, mainly aphides and scale-insects. The lacewing larva is not only diminutive but also has the macabre habit of camouflaging itself with the dry husks of its latest victims, which it flicks over its head onto its bristle-covered body.

The myriad kinds of gall growths which adorn oak leaves and

21

twigs are commonly the work of insects, despite their inanimate appearance. Oak 'apples', as big as a tenpenny piece, and smaller oak marble galls both result from the activities of various Hymenopterid wasp larvae eating the young leaf buds; the gall accretion results from an automatic defence response of the tree, much as a blister is caused on the skin when we burn ourselves. Oak-apples are a delicate pale green and pinkish red colour at the outset but turn dark brown with age, when one will find them peppered with tiny holes whence the adult wasps emerged. The whiskery reddish 'Robin's pin-cushion' or Bedeguar galls, common on wild rose, are caused in the same way by Hymenopterid wasps. They also turn hard and woody after the insects have left them.

Abandoned gall growth caused by larvae of a Gall-wasp (*Rhodites rosae*) —'Robin's pin-cushion'. Actual size.

Many of the smaller galls which mottle the undersides of oak leaves give the impression of some dreadful contagious disease, but again each contains a minute gall-wasp larva, and sometimes unrelated 'guests' which are simply using the gall growth as a shelter and feeding base. Each affected leaf thus becomes something of an insect city in its own right.

Of the many hundreds of gall growths of different kinds, most of them peculiar to particular plants, some are not the work of truly indigenous British insects. The gall-wasp *Andricus kollari* is one such alien; it causes oak marble gall and apparently first became

22

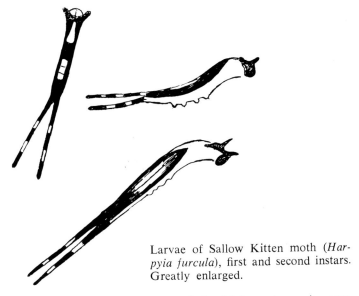

Larvae of Sallow Kitten moth (*Harpyia furcula*), first and second instars. Greatly enlarged.

established here during the latter part of the 18th century. A more recent importation is *Andricus quercus-calicis*, an insect of similar habits but producing a differently shaped gall structure, reminiscent of a multi-faceted mediaeval mace. This particular gall-maker seems to have appeared first in the 1960s in the Midlands, from which it spread steadily east and south, and also to the south-west, especially in Devon.

While less afflicted than oaks, willows and sallows (*Salix*) also have their complement of gall growths, as well as a variety of insects feeding more conspicuously. Sallows in particular can often be relied upon, at least in the south of England, to reveal the caterpillars of such evocatively named moth species as Puss, Sallow Kitten, Herald and Coxcomb Prominent. The caterpillars of these species are not always easy to pick out, being mainly if not wholly green and moving little during the daytime. The eggs from which they hatch are even more difficult to find, especially those of the Puss and Sallow Kitten moths; unlike the others, these are deposited in ones or twos instead of in close-packed batches. Nevertheless, one *can* find them, as I have done, by carefully examining each individual leaf. The eggs are usually, though not invariably, laid on the underside.

Great sallows or goat willows (*Salix capraea*) have a particularly soft spot in my affections; low and shrubby, they allow systematic examination without giving one a crick in the neck; they also seem to come up with something different on every visit. It was on sallow, a few years ago, that I met with the breathtaking sight of two caterpillars, of different species but equally spectacular in appearance, clinging toe-to-toe to the same twig. The upper one was the larva of a Grey Dagger moth (*Apatele psi*), gorgeously arrayed in red, black and white, with a broad yellow line down the middle of its double-humped back. Below, dwarfing it in size if not outshining it in beauty, was the plump three-inch long caterpillar of a Puss moth (*Cerura vinula*) whose rich velvety green body bore a contrasting white-edged dull purple saddle along the back; its large pale brown head was encircled with scarlet, while a pair of bright red 'whips' extruded from the twin spiky tails, probably as a warning to predators.

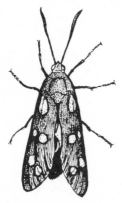

Six-spot Burnet moth (*Zygaena filipendulae*). Enlarged × 2 approx.

If one is unlikely to come across this sort of chance association very often during one's entomologizing, it does show that the most ordinary and accessible places can be among the most profitable hunting-grounds. Neither the Puss nor the Grey Dagger is rare.

Nor is sallow their only food plant. The Puss occurs just as frequently on willow and sometimes poplar, and the Grey Dagger feeds on several common plants such as lime, blackthorn, hawthorn and wild apple, which are frequently found in hedgerows together with other species such as wild rose and field maple. These valuable woodland substitutes are likely to produce as many insect species as any other habitat. They are also convenient to observe since one can simply walk along slowly examining the leafage at or below head height. This is excellent training for the eye, and certainly far better than the drastic *beating* of shrubs recommended as a short-cut by many entomologists. A disadvantage of beating is that if the hedgerow is tangled and intertwined, it is not always possible to know from which plants the insects have been dislodged.

Sometimes, in May, the leafage of hawthorn, wild rose and blackthorn (sloe) is so liberally covered with the finely hairy brilliant scarlet, white and black caterpillars of the Yellow Tail moth (*Euproctis similis*) as to suggest that all the female moths in the neighbourhood had concentrated their efforts here. Here, too, will probably be the looper-type larva of the Magpie moth (*Abraxas grossulariata*), which also turns up from time to time on cultivated gooseberries and currants. Thin and stick-like in appearance, it is unlike most Geometrid larvae in being strikingly patterned— spotted with bright yellow and black on a chalky white background. Curiously enough, the moth itself has precisely the same colour scheme, while even the pupa, slung up in a loose cocoon between leaves, is shiny black, banded with yellow. Presumably, these con- trasting colours act as a warning of distastefulness to colour- perceptive birds, in the same way as the more garish tints of some other moth species.

Wild-rose blossoms are always attractive to nectar-seeking insects, and may entice the Pearl Bordered Fritillary (*Boloria euphrosyne*) in woodland clearings. Hornets, too, have a way of gravitating here, as well as little Wasp beetles, whose black and yellow pattern and jerky movements effectively mimic those of a wasp, thus presenting an example of what is known as Batesian mimicry, after the 19th-

25

Wasp beetle (*Clytus arietis*). Almost actual size.

century naturalist of that name. Many of the little hover-flies (*Syrphidae*) which visit hedgerow flowers—their curious legless larvae feed on the aphides that afflict our roses—are of particular beauty, but rarely receive the attention they deserve. Some are banded black and orange or yellow, with brilliant tinsel-like wings and wonderfully polished bodies that reflect the sunlight like burnished metal. They are also the most accomplished aeronauts, being able to hover with their bodies almost motionless while feeding, and turn and tack in all directions at amazing speed.

The vegetation beneath a hedge or in a lush meadow is always worth careful investigation, for places of this sort tend to support a different insect population. Little Black-and-Red Froghoppers (*Cercopis vulnerata*) may bestride a grass frond, ready to put distance between themselves and you with a powerful kick of their hind legs (note how they raise their front legs just before they leap). A furry Drinker moth caterpillar (*Philudoria potatoria*), its brown, yellow and white hairs resembling some deep-welted fireside rug, could be clinging motionless along a haulm, falling to the ground at a touch. Grasshoppers leap wildly to avoid one's footstep, while little grass and plume moths float away as lightly as thistledown. Here indeed is another world: a miniature world one can properly appreciate only by getting down literally to its level. It is a good idea to do just that, by selecting a small area of low vegetation, then crouching or sitting beside it and allowing the eye to adjust to the smaller scale of life down there. It is surprising how often your patience is rewarded with the unusual, not merely in the different insects that present themselves to view, but in the

Caterpillars of the Kentish Glory moth (*Endromis versicolora*) in threat posture. The tail claspers attached to the birch stem look like a second head, perhaps confusing attacking predators. Greatly enlarged.   (*G. E. Hyde*)

little instances of behaviour that might have been missed had you just glanced and passed on. For example, I recall one memorable occasion when I was idly contemplating a tiny half-inch-long looper caterpillar busily chewing the narrow clustered petals of a species of hardheads (*Centaurea*). This, in itself, was nothing unusual, but what happened next was pure delight. A piece of frass of precisely the same tint as the petals appearing at its tail end, the caterpillar doubled upon itself in an instant, seized the offending item in its jaws and dropped it overboard! Incidents of this sort are rarely recorded in the literature, but they can be seen by anyone who takes the trouble to get down and look for them.

3

OUT OF SIGHT?

In H. G. Wells's *The First Men in the Moon*, the Grand Lunar, ruler of all the Selenites, comments upon the 'strange superficiality and unreasonableness of man' for living on the mere surface of his world. He would have regarded insects with more approval for, like the Selenites, they occur in considerable numbers and variety underground, some spending all their lives in this strange twilight world, others living there only as immature forms.

Many insects that live entirely below the soil surface are extremely minute, colourless and etiolated. Some, like the tiny Proturans, scarcely more than a millimetre or two in length, are in fact quite blind and lacking in antennae, the sensory role of these appendages being apparently assumed by the forelegs. Easily overlooked as they are, it is scarcely surprising that these fascinating 'primitives' have been very little studied. The same may be said of the pure white *Campodea*, which a sharp eye may sometimes discern scuttling rapidly through the disturbed soil. Eyeless like the Protura, it nevertheless has long antennae and a pair of thread-like tail filaments, yet its total length is rarely more than about a third of an inch. Not infrequently, *Campodea* is found lurking in the tunnels of the nests of Black Garden ants (*Lasius niger*), where it appears to be tolerated as a scavenger.

A number of larger insects spend their larval days in the soil, but on maturing tend to move up a floor as it were and become more surface-dwelling. Prominent among these are larvae of ground-

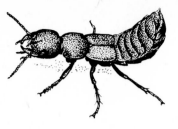

Devil's Coach-horse beetle (*Ocypus olens*). Enlarged × 2 approx.

and rove-beetles, whitish and soft of body, unlike their armoured progenitors, but armed with equally powerful, needle-sharp mandibles for securing prey. As with all soil-dwellers, their below-stairs existence is vitally important on two counts: the soil prevents their developing bodies from becoming dried out and also shields them to some extent from the prying eyes of birds and insectivorous mammals such as shrews. Not all escape even then, and other insects are liable to treat them as fair game, except that the initial attack is likely to be effected in a far more subtle manner.

With luck, one can sometimes discover examples of this dog-eats-dog predation, as I once did during a spell of garden digging. Having broken a large clod of soil, I found within it a smooth oval chamber containing the larva of what was probably a Devil's

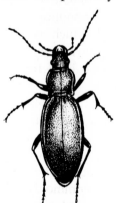

Rove beetle (*Ocypus sp.*) a close relative of the Devil's Coach-horse (*O. olens*). Enlarged × 2 approx.
Violet Ground beetle (*Carabus violaceus*). About actual size. A scuttling ground predator that spends much of its time lurking under stones, old logs, etc.

Coach-horse beetle (*Ocypus olens*). Attached along its whole length was a row of white, goblin-like pupae: the progeny of a species of parasitic chalcid wasp which had evidently managed to catch her fierce victim off-guard and lay her eggs in its soft abdomen, perhaps by means of a single insertion. Possibly the larva was parasitized while changing its skin, otherwise it is hard to imagine that it would have submitted to such unwelcome attentions without putting up a fight! It is one of the subtleties of nature that the victim does not die immediately after being 'stung' in this way; the wasp larvae feed on its internal tissues in such a way as to keep it alive, and therefore fresh, just long enough for them to complete their own metamorphosis, while arresting that of their host. The incredible precision of the whole operation is heightened by the fact that the adult parasites emerge from the now lifeless husk all at once—in this particular instance (for I kept the afflicted larva) *twenty-two* of them!

It is always assumed that rove- and ground-beetles are very much the gardener's allies, both as adults and larvae. But they probably do not discriminate too much. I myself have found the adult beetles feeding on woodlice, spiders, caterpillars of various sorts, and even snails, which is a bit of a mixture because woodlice are innocuous scavengers, and spiders of course are positively useful. There can be little room for doubt, however, about some other beetle larvae which turn up in the soil from time to time. The fat white, but brown-headed, grubs of the Cockchafer (*Melolontha melolontha*), shiny orange or brown wireworms (larvae of click-beetles), and soft greyish leatherjackets (cranefly larvae) are all likely to chew the roots of cultivated plants, as well as those of unwanted weeds. The same can be said of those fat Noctuid moth caterpillars commonly called 'cut-worms' on account of their irritating habit of nipping off seedling plants just below the surface of the ground. If they are missed at the larval stage, the spade may later turn up their pupae, together perhaps with those of Dot (*Melanchra persicariae*) and Cabbage moths (*Mamestra brassicae*).

When I was a boy at school, we would compete for the much

31

larger pupae which we sometimes found beneath a row of poplars, elms and limes. The caterpillars of our two commonest species of hawk moths, the Lime and Poplar (*Mimas tiliae, Laothoe populi*), feed on the foliage of the trees that give them their names, as well as on sallows, and both are easy to find because they weave their frail and easily ruptured cocoons only just beneath the fallen leaves in autumn—the action of the rake is often sufficient to expose them. Larvae of the Eyed hawk (*Smerinthus ocellata*), not infrequently found on apple and plum trees, and Privet hawks (*Sphinx ligustri*) burrow quite deeply before pupating; so too does the caterpillar of the spectacular great Death's Head hawk (*Acherontia atropos*). One will be fortunate to find *atropos* larvae or pupae in the average garden plot, although this strongly-flying migrant turns up nearly every year, more especially on the south and east coasts. Not unnaturally the fertile females much prefer to lay their eggs on massed potato tops rather than on the less easily found nightshades (*Solanaceae*), tea-tree (*Lycium barbarum*), snowberry (*Symphoricarpus*), and some others which form their alternative food plants. Unfortunately, the two-inch-plus mahogany-coloured pupae rarely survive our winters, perhaps partly because they are so often damaged or scuffed out of their protective cocoons during potato harvesting.

Entomologists are fortunate people, not merely in the number of species they can study but because there are few habitats which do not support at least some insects, even in winter. For example, one storey up from the soil itself, the undersides of large firmly set stones and logs, or the peeling bark of felled trees and tree-stumps, are likely to display almost as large a quota of insects as a woodland glade in high summer. Not infrequently, shelters of this sort will reveal intriguing aggregations of insects of the same species, as if they had a sort of social instinct, though the species are not social in the sense that ants, bees and wasps are. Ladybirds

The 'woolly bear' caterpillar of the Garden Tiger moth (*Arctia caja*) which overwinters and recommences feeding in the spring on a variety of low-growing plants. Greatly enlarged. (*G. E. Hyde*)

are well known to hibernate in large packed clusters, perhaps of several hundreds, and other species apparently find similar comfort in numbers, whereas in other circumstances they are relatively solitary in their habits. Adult Devil's Coach-horse beetles (whose larvae I mentioned earlier) are most often found singly during the day, perhaps lurking under a piece of wood or old sack; when disturbed they stand firm, with legs straddled, tail-end raised and jaws agape as if defying further liberties. From time to time I have found these sooty-black beetles in groups of three or four under a large flagstone, presumably investigating its potential as a communal spot for hibernation. Smaller members of the extensive rove-beetle family display similar social tendencies, such as species of the genus *Stenus*; I have found up to fifteen of these tiny large-eyed beetles massed together beneath a plank by a water-filled sandpit. A more spectacular discovery some years ago was of seven of the inch-long, beautiful bronze-purple ground beetle *Carabus granulatus*, hibernating under the peeling bark of a fallen elm. Each had fashioned for itself a roomy chamber in the dead, burnt-brown inner bark tissue, although two of them—a mated pair perhaps—shared one compartment.

Certain solitary ichneumon wasps, many of which parasitize the caterpillars of butterflies and moths, also tend to hibernate socially, one of the larger and more conspicuous species being *Perispudus facialis*, a particularly goggle-eyed species, and distinctive in that its incessantly twiddling antennae are banded with white in the centre. Ichneumons are among those many insects whose habits and life history are relatively little known—maybe at least partly because they cause so many disappointments to butterfly and moth breeders!

Of the true social insects, the bees, wasps and ants, only the queens survive the summer nest; having previously mated, they sleep away the winter ready to found an entirely new colony the following summer. Fat queen wasps are commonly found in winter clinging to the undersides of peeling tree bark, or maybe even up in the corner of a room. Some people regard queen-wasp-killing

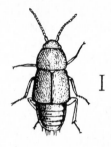

I

A Staphylinid beetle of the genus
Tachinus; a frequently encountered inhabitant of decaying fungi. Greatly
enlarged.

almost as a matter of honour, but any harm these insects do is
probably at least partly balanced by their value as pest controllers.
In the early part of the summer, when there are developing larvae
in the comb, worker wasps are primarily carnivorous, collecting
a variety of insects for their protein-hungry charges to feed on.
A careful observer can often see them capture and carry away all
kinds of larvae, as well as aphides and small flies, often biting and
chewing them all over before flying off—which is sometimes done
with difficulty if the prey is large. I have even seen wasps chewing
at the flesh of a dead blackbird, in company with bluebottle and
greenbottle flies, whose own object was doubtless of a very different
kind: to lay their eggs in the decomposing flesh.

Distasteful as it may seem to non-entomologists, animal carcases
are always worth examining since many insects scavenge on such
material and thus incidentally perform a useful service as refuse
disposers. Sometimes your arrival at such rich sources of material
—rich both for insects and those who study them—comes too late
for the more interesting species, and all you find is a seething,
writhing mass of flesh-fly larvae. It is probably partly a matter of
who gets their first, for there is always great competition among
the different insect groups and species for pickings. Small black
carrion beetles are often numerous, and there may also be rove-
beetles of various sorts, such as the small but handsome *Staphylinus
caesareus*, with reddish wing-covers and black and white abdomen.
Larger and altogether more formidable are the big shiny black

35

Robber-fly (family *Asilidae*) with its damselfly prey. Robber-flies are predatory Dipterids which capture other insects, often much larger than themselves,
piercing their tissues and sucking them dry.   *(Robin Fletcher)*

or black-and-orange Burying or Sexton beetles, which have a
particularly sure nose for carrion. They seek out on powerful wings
any newly dead animals—mammals, birds, reptiles and so forth—
and immediately start to prepare them for consumption by their
future progeny, chewing and moulding the flesh into a more accept-
able consistency and shape and also excavating the soil beneath
the carcase so that it sinks down and eventually becomes completely
covered and protected from competitors such as flies. Both mating
and egg-laying take place near the corpse and are often accompanied
by much excited squeaking.

One of the fascinations of observing insects' behaviour, and
their presence in certain situations, is that it can lead you, Holmes-
like, in quite unexpected directions. I was once examining the
entrance to a badgers' sett when I noticed a *Necrophorus* burying
beetle steadily negotiating the slope towards the light and open air.
It would be too much to suggest that the beetle wore a self-satisfied
look, but having previously had suspicions about the fate of this
particular badger colony I was now pretty well confirmed in them.
Badgers rarely, if ever, take food actually into the sett, and this led

me to conclude that the badgers themselves were dead—which would be the beetle's reason for entering their domain. It is always worth thinking along these lines when looking for and at insects—asking yourself just *why* they happen to be where they are—since it can lead to a greater understanding of them and their place in nature.

The inter-relationships and habits of aquatic insects present a whole new subject for investigation; but since many species spend most of their time beneath the surface it is often difficult to observe them *in situ*. However, setting pond-dipping apart, there is always much to be seen in summer on the surface of a stretch of still water and its immediate neighbourhood. I myself am always fascinated by the incessant twisting and turning of the little Whirligig beetles (*Gyrinus*) on the water's surface, their highly polished bodies reflecting the glare of the sun. Why they constantly gyrate is not altogether clear, although it has been suggested that the habit serves to concentrate their search for minute items of food; their large numbers probably make for greater *individual* safety. *Gyrinus* has its middle and hind legs specially developed and paddle-like, and fringed with hairs to help it swim. Certain larger water beetles are less specialised in this direction. The Great Silver beetle (*Hydrophilus piceus*), which rivals the terrestrial Stag beetle in size, is a particularly poor swimmer. Like the Great Diving beetle (*Dytiscus marginalis*), it can occasionally be seen when it comes to the surface from time to time to take in air. The larvae behave similarly, and have a pair of terminal siphons to break the surface film.

These insects, together with many species of bugs, like Water Boatmen, spend practically all their time in the water, except when necessity (such as the drying up of their home) causes them to colonise new territories. Others, however, are aquatic only in their development stage. Mosquitoes and gnats, mayflies, stone-flies, caddis-flies, alder-flies are just a few of these insect amphibians, but undoubtedly the most spectacular of them all are the dragon-flies and damsel-flies, the former zooming purposefully, the latter fluttering weakly, over almost any suitable stretch of water. Little blue- and black-banded damsel-flies are particularly common along canal banks, while occasionally one may be fortunate enough to see a superb male Banded Agrion (*Agrion splendens*), its bluish translucent wings bearing a wide band of deep storm-cloud blue; the female lacks this distinctive addition to her colour scheme. Damsel-fly and dragonfly nymphs generally spend several years at the bottom of pond and lake, feeding on other insects, worms, tadpoles and the like, before finally crawling up a reed frond and transforming into the aerial 'dragon'. One can often find these insects' abandoned outer skins or exuvial cases still affixed to the vegetation, where they provide the student with the opportunity to examine the casing of the curious *labrum* which is hinged beneath the head and thrust forward to secure prey. This structure is lost during the change to adult insect, although the adult dragonflies themselves are equally predacious without it.

There is still much superstition surrounding dragonflies, emanating from the idea that these impressive insects have a sting for the unwary at the end of their—or at least the females'—pointed abdomens. Although this is a myth, it does bring to mind certain other insect groups which can and do sting, stab or bite man, and thus force themselves upon his attention. Literally irritating as it is, the action of admitted nuisances like fleas, lice, bed-bugs, horse-flies and mosquitoes is not inspired by malevolence. It is simply that their physiology demands a feed of mammalian blood before they can breed successfully. It requires a certain degree of scientific detachment to see beauty in such groups as these; yet there is much to be admired in the marvellous precision with which the insect blood-suckers carry out their work. Incidentally, if you can restrain your swatting hand long enough to allow a close look at the eyes of a horse-fly, you will see that they are often very beautiful: banded in green, red and other colours, and of a satin-like lustre, although this quickly fades after death.

Many insects will stab or bite if carelessly handled but this action, when applied to ourselves, is purely defensive. Nevertheless,

Silk-button galls on oak leaf, caused by the gall wasp *Neuroterus numismalis*. Each gall contains a single larva, which pupates there and produces a female gall wasp (only). Adult females lay their eggs parthenogenetically (i.e. without mating) in oak leaf buds, producing blister galls which produce both males and females early the following summer. *(Alan W. Heath)*

those who have been stung by wasps or stabbed by a Water Boatman (*Notonecta*) will not need to be told that the effects can be extremely painful. The boatman pumps a digestive enzyme into its victims—normally tadpoles or other aquatic insects—by means of its stabbing *rostrum* or mouth-tube, which is one reason why its wound is so painful to humans. By contrast with these poison-injectors, the mouth-parts of adult carnivorous beetles are designed to allow them to secure and rend their prey, which is then passed into the mouth piecemeal by means of finger-like palps. These scuttling predators need to be treated with respect, as I know from experimenting with the European *Carabus auronitens*. I found that it could pierce toughish paper with ease!

Insects like these are unlikely to bother us much unless we interfere with *them*, but it is a sobering thought that circumstances can change certain species' habits from the innocuous to the troublesome. During the long dry summer of 1976, for example, people began to complain that even the universally popular lady-birds were settling on them and nipping, if not actually piercing, their flesh. This outrageous behaviour seems to have resulted from a combination of unusual factors: a population explosion of lady-birds and a consequent diminution of their aphis food supply, plus a lack of moisture. It was not that they had suddenly turned to feeding on man, but presumably they found salty human sweat attractive.

A milder and far commoner nuisance is often evident during summer when outdoor people—cricketers for example—will often note minute blackish insects weaving their way through the hairs on sweaty arms and legs. Mostly they will be thrips, insects best known to the gardener from their habit of sucking the juices of flower heads and vegetables. During hot weather the air is often full of these tiny aeronauts, and it is inevitable that some will settle on us, although the worst that can be said of them is that they cause a mild short-lived tickling. Rather more disconcerting is the tendency of some insects to make a sort of 'kami-kazi' flight into the eye. Few people give these hapless midgets more than a brief glance after they have been picked out on the corner of a handker-chief, except to dismiss them as some sort of fly. Sometimes the intruder is indeed a Dipterid of sorts, but more often than not examination under a glass will reveal that it is a Staphylinid or rove-beetle, closely allied to the Devil's Coach-horse and almost exactly matching it in everything but size. Like its bigger relative, it can exude a pungent fluid from glands at the tip of the abdomen, which doubtless explains why it often irritates or inflames the eye temporarily.

4

NOW YOU HEAR IT . . .

That continual hum of insect activity, so typical of a hot summer's day in woodland glade and along hedgerow, can initially be confusing, even soporific, in its impression upon the brain. Its 'blanket' effect tends to obscure the fact that it is made up of a myriad individual sounds, many of which can be analysed and identified. A large number of insects produce sounds, and some of them at least are as diagnostic as the songs and calls of birds.

Many insect sounds are largely if not wholly involuntary and automatic. They vary according to the insect's speed of flight and rapidity of wing-beat, the size and shape of its wings, and so forth; but even so, the powerful hum of a Dor beetle is quite different in character from the steady monotone of the drone-fly, and the angry buzz of a wasp is sufficiently unlike the high-pitched whine of a mosquito for us to know what has passed or is threatening us. Beekeepers claim to be able to recognise a difference in the sounds made by queen and worker honey-bees in the hive; indeed it is said that the sound of the queen is not made by her wings but by air being forced through the spiracles or breathing-holes along the sides of her body. Certain flies are believed to produce sounds in a somewhat similar manner. However, these phenomena have been little studied, and purely wing-produced sounds soon tend to confuse our auditory sense. Few of us, for example, would be able to tell for certain, without actually seeing it, whether it was a wasp or a bee that had been trapped inside the front-room window, and our

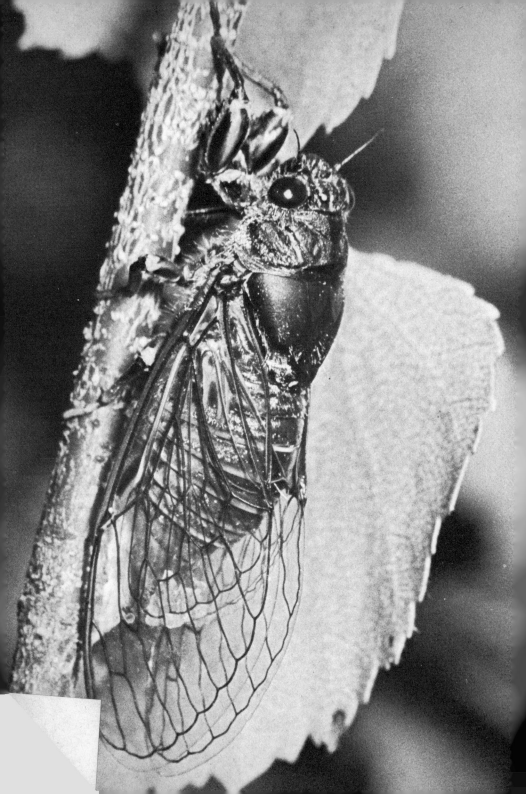

relatively inefficient hearing usually makes it impossible for us to distinguish the sounds of different wasps and bees.

The human listener is at a much greater advantage with insects that produce sounds 'consciously' and deliberately, like the crickets and grasshoppers. Made almost solely by the males, basically for the purposes of courtship, the calls of most British species of Orthoptera are to a high degree distinctive, though they nevertheless present more of a challenge to the ear than do the truly vocal songs of a chiffchaff or wren. The Orthoptera are the true musicians of the insect world and their music—if it may be called that—is produced by precisely the same method, in principle, as that of the human strings-player. The sounds are caused by *stridulation,* involving friction—the violinist's or cellist's bow and strings being directly analogous to the insect's 'file' and 'scraper', where one part of the body is drawn over or rubbed against another. Not all species use the same parts of the body for this purpose; indeed, the different methods of stridulation form one of the bases for separating the long-antennaed crickets and bush-crickets from the short-horned grasshoppers.

Grasshoppers are perhaps the more extrovert performers. Typically denizens of meadow and scrub, they produce their songs by rubbing the upper (thigh) part of their long hind legs against a hardened vein on their wing-covers; usually the two legs work together, in unison or alternately. Crickets and bush-crickets employ a more subtle and less discernible method, one wing-cover, or *tegmen*, being rubbed or scraped against another which it overlaps. Anyone who has listened to a cricket, and compared its 'song' with that of the Common Green grasshopper (*Omocestus viridulus*), for example, will probably agree that the sounds made by the cricket are less

Male New Forest cicada (*Cicadetta montana*). Male cicadas 'sing' by means of a pair of special membranes, or tymbals, situated at the sides of the abdomen, near the thorax, and beneath the wings; females are quite silent. Both male and female are about one inch long, the female being a fraction larger and sturdier. So far as is known *C. montana* is confined to the New Forest. *(J. A. Grant)* gratingly harsh than those of the grasshopper, though they are often tedious and monotonous to Western ears if heard for a long period. It is perhaps significant that in China and Japan, and some other countries, where Orthoptera were once widely kept as singing pets, their varying musical abilities being compared and contrasted, most of the favoured species belonged either to the *Gryllidae* (true crickets) or the *Tettigonidae* (bush-crickets); only a few species of grasshoppers were thought entertaining to the oriental ear.

But of course the songs of these insect violinists are not designed for human hearing. They are mainly of purely sexual significance: a means of bringing the two sexes together. With few exceptions, the songs are produced by the male, and fetch his partner—who comes running and jumping and in some cases flying. There are variations on this general theme, because the male is often singing in direct competition with several others, varying these renderings with 'threat' songs when a rival encroaches upon his territory. Then, again, a quite different song, softer and gentler, is frequently produced during courtship. The whole business is remarkably similar to the conduct of birds during the mating season.

Both male and female crickets and grasshoppers are able to hear and appreciate the subtle differences between these and other sounds by means of a pair of special tympanic membranes which vibrate and transmit messages to the brain in much the same way as our eardrums do. The actual positioning of the tympana on the insects' bodies, and the methods of stridulation, differ enough to distinguish one group from another. In the crickets and bush-crickets, the 'ear' is situated on the inside of each of the forelegs, these commonly being extended forward, particularly during challenging between males. By contrast, grasshoppers may turn their whole bodies broadside-on when listening, since their tympana are on the side of the abdomen, between the first and second pair of legs.

Britain has only thirty species of Orthoptera, and many of these have been reduced by pesticides, destruction of habitat, and so on.

One of the odd-men-out of the Orthoptera: a ground-hopper, *Tetrix undulata*, close relative of the grasshoppers, which does not stridulate like its brethren, at least not audibly to the human ear. *(J. A. Grant)*

Some have probably always had only a local distribution, though they may be common enough where they occur. The small, rapidly-moving Wood cricket (*Nemobius sylvestris*), for example, is often numerous in regions like the New Forest of Hampshire, where colonies may be discovered under leaf litter and rotting logs, in ditches and similar places. The much larger, shiny black Field cricket (*Gryllus campestris*) is considerably rarer, being restricted to meadowland in parts of Sussex and Hampshire. This is the species whose song the eighteenth-century parson-naturalist Gilbert White described as 'irksome' when 'confined in a paper cage and set in the sun'. The effect is somewhat different when the insect is free, probably superior to the shrill grating of the House cricket (*Acheta domesticus*) which may now be as common on large refuse dumps, where it scavenges for scraps, as in houses.

Another species sadly reduced to the status of rarity is the intriguing Mole cricket (*Gryllotalpa gryllotalpa*). This species has

Mole cricket (*Gryllotalpa gryllotalpa*). Enlarged × 1½ approx.

been allocated a family (*Gryllotalpidae*) all to itself, and indeed it is very different from all other British Orthoptera, with its heavy, dark-brown, somewhat tubular body and huge rounded thorax. The Mole cricket's vernacular name derives from the shape of its forelegs, which resemble those of a mole and differ to a remarkable degree from the other two pairs in being flattened and shovel-like, with pointed projections, beautifully adapted for digging in the soil wherein it makes its home. The Mole cricket's song, which is delivered from the mouth of the burrow, is also highly idiosyncratic. Some think it resembles the grating whirr made by a fisherman's reel. A sustained sound with occasional short pauses and changes of pitch, it is not altogether unlike the call of a nightjar; some people could well confuse the two, particularly since both are heard after dark. Nowadays, unfortunately, one is far more likely to hear the summer-visiting nightjar than a Mole cricket since there are definite records of the latter's recent occurrence only in Hampshire, Wiltshire and Cheshire although, since few of our Orthoptera have been properly mapped, it may occur elsewhere.

Learning to distinguish between the songs and calls of our crickets and grasshoppers takes practice and something of a musical ear, but it is well worth attempting, whether in the company of an expert orthopterist or with the help of the several excellent gramophone records now available, such as that issued as a companion to Dr David Ragge's fine monograph on the group (listed in 'Selected Further Reading'). Lacking such help, verbal descriptions of the songs, while obviously a second-best, are not without

46

value, as a pamphlet on crickets and grasshoppers, published in 1975 by the British Naturalists' Association, vividly demonstrates. In it, Christopher Haes (who has long specialised in these singing insects) employs similes and comparisons to convey the different character of each species' song. These seem to me to combine the interests of naturalist and litterateur in a most effective way. The song of the Stripe-winged grasshopper (*Stenobothrus lineatus*), for example, he describes as having 'a strange nasal pulsating "bee-in-spider's-web" sound'. That of the Heath grasshopper (*Chorthippus vagans*) is, according to Haes, 'like a tiny duck quacking quickly', and he calls the song of the Meadow grasshopper (*Chorthippus parallelus*) 'a short repeated chuckle'. Best of all, perhaps, is his description of the call of the Rufous grasshopper (*Gomphocerippus rufus*) as being 'like a tiny clockwork toy running down'. Imaginative writing of this kind both appeals to the non-naturalist, encouraging him to take an interest, and also helps towards identification.

It is one thing to identify a song—but often quite another problem to track the insect down to its singing position or lair, especially when one discovers that certain species are accomplished ventriloquists! Entomologists frequently tell of almost literally running around in circles trying to locate the source of the sounds, as I did only recently when trying to find a House cricket which was performing in the courtyard below my flat. Standing still, I would be quite positive that the sound came from side A; but after stealthily gaining that position I became equally convinced that the shrillings came from sides B or C; and so it went on each time I followed my auditory nose in a different direction. All this is linked to the ability of the insect to change the pitch or the volume of its call, by altering the rate of production or raising and lowering its sound-amplifying tegmina, thus misleading the listener.

In fact the sounds produced by certain Orthoptera are so high-pitched as to be inaudible to many people with otherwise clinically normal hearing. In just the same way men and women, particularly

47

over the age of about forty, may find themselves unable to hear the squeak of a bat, although they may have been able to do so when younger.

The difficulty of inaudibility is even more marked in the case of the only British species of cicada: one of a group of Homopterid bugs more typical of tropical climes. So far as is known, the New Forest cicada (*Cicadetta montana*) does not occur in Britain outside a few localities in that area. But then its song (again produced only by the male) is usually pitched so high—up to 16 kilocycles a second (or 16 Kilo-Hertz)—that many a seeker may easily pass it by, which is strange when one thinks of the deafening chorus produced by many foreign cicadas, whose jangling, nerve-shattering songs must have made many a westerner long for the quieter ambience of the English countryside.

I myself have been fortunate enough both to hear and see the New Forest cicada at close quarters on several occasions. However, I began with a distinct advantage: I knew where to look. Even then, it took considerable practice at the outset to attune my ear to the peculiar character of the call. Basically, it is not unlike a thin jet of steam or gas escaping from a cylinder: relatively monotonous in character. It is moreover only emitted on hot still days, particularly when the air is humid and still. The effect on

Female New Forest cicada (*Cicadetta montana*) simultaneously feeding from, and ovipositing in, a tree stem. Slightly enlarged.

the ear and brain is often extremely peculiar. Sometimes it is as if you suddenly become aware that you are hearing it without positively being able to say 'That's it'; as if indeed it actually originated *within* your head, like a ringing in the ears . . .

My very first physical encounter with *Cicadetta montana* was what might well be called beginner's luck. I not merely tracked the insect down to its singing perch by means of its song, but actually discovered the performer clinging to its pine-tree perch at about head-height. This is most unusual, since the cicada is usually quick to cease singing at the investigator's approach and either make off by low, fast, direct flight to a safer spot or shuffle around to the opposite side of the tree bole, away from the questing eye. I must have happened upon this particular individual directly after it had emerged from its nymphal husk, possibly before it had made its maiden flight.

Cicadas are among those many insects which spend much longer as developing larvae, or nymphs, than they do as adults. *Cicadetta montana* almost certainly takes several years to reach maturity whereas the adults may live for only a few weeks. Add to this the fact that the nymphs are subterranean in habit, feeding on the roots of various plants, such as purple moor grass (*Molinia coerulea*), and it is easy to appreciate that the species could have been overlooked in many of its habitats. J. A. Grant, a professional entomologist who has been studying cicadas for many years, feels our only native cicada could well occur over a much wider area of the New Forest and just possibly in suitable deciduous woodlands elsewhere. As with many of our crickets and grasshoppers, therefore, it is well worth keeping an ear cocked for this elusive insect.

Except for its more pronounced continuity, the cicada's song is not very dissimilar in basic character to the sounds made by some of the totally unrelated Orthoptera, but the mode of production certainly differs. No stridulation is involved here, but a type of percussion instrument. On each side of the cicada's body, beneath the wings, is a moderately large membrane to which special

Sketches of New Forest cicada (*Cica-detta montana*) including female's ovi-positor. Slightly enlarged.

muscles are attached. In sound-making, these muscles are alter-nately contracted and expanded, thus pushing the membrane out-wards and inwards to produce a series of clicks which are emitted so rapidly as to be virtually indistinguishable as individual sounds, except when recorded and played back slowly. It is rather like those clacking tin lids which boys used to make years ago: a piece of string, knotted at one end, is pushed through the centre of the lid and alternately pulled and released. So far as I know, there is no more sophisticated musical instrument which works on the same principle.

While the insects mentioned so far are the real music masters of the insect world, they are not the only ones to produce sounds deliberately. Certain beetles and Heteropterid bugs can stridulate. A typical example is the aquatic Screech beetle (*Hydrobius fuscipes*), which makes a squeak by rubbing the undersides of its wing-cases against the abdomen beneath. It will do this when captured in a net and more particularly in the water where it pro-bably squeaks to attract the opposite sex since water is an excellent sound-conductor. Another water denizen, the Lesser Water Boat-man (*Corixa*), can also call a partner, in this case by scraping its rostrum, or piercing mouth-tube, against the groove in which it rests when not in use.

Other unexpected sound-producers are terrestrial. For example, the little Wasp beetle (*Clytus arietis*) adds to its accomplished wasp-like disguise by audibly rubbing its legs against the sides of its wing-covers, probably to deter predators, the result being a thin reedy squeak not unlike someone blowing gently on a grass blade.

It is but one of several species of Longhorn beetle than can stridulate. I have already mentioned the tendency of Sexton or Burying
beetles to 'vocalise' after gathering at animal carcases, while stridulation is also an accomplishment of the little predatory assassin-
bugs that roam ground and foliage in search of invertebrate prey.
Even certain species of ants are said to be able to stridulate, and
can also produce a clicking sound with their mandibles.

More curiously, the larvae of certain ground-dwelling and wood-
boring beetles stridulate when in their tunnels. Here the purpose
is obscure, unless it is to warn other larvae of the same species
to get out of the way. It seems likely that the sounds are received
as vibrations on the body hairs because the larva has no other
obvious reception mechanism.

One of the most curious examples of sound-producing insects
is the great Death's Head hawk-moth (*Acherontia atropos*). The
moth itself can utter a shrill squeak by forcing air through an
aperature at the base of its short proboscis. The insect is fond of
honey and it is said (but with no real evidence) that the sound
pacifies the bees when the moth enters a hive to rob the combs.
Whether the supposition is true or not, it can have done little to
lessen the superstitious awe in which the species was held in the
past, mainly on account of the distinctive skull-like markings on
its thorax. Equally remarkable is the fact that the Death's Head's
caterpillar can also produce sounds. It makes a peculiar clicking
when handled too freely, probably by grinding the plates of its
mouth-parts together. It is worth adding that the size and consequent hearty appetite of the Death's Head caterpillar make the
sounds of its eating easily audible!

A good many sounds made by insects are not entirely self-made
or idiomatic, but depend on certain situations and surroundings.
The half-inch Death-watch beetle (*Xestobium rufovillosum*), for
example, seems something of a masochist, for it deliberately
knocks its head against the sides of its larval tunnellings, presumably to attract a female with a view to mating. Since these beetles
are most commonly found in old wooden beams and large furniture

(though I once found an adult under the bark of an ancient willow) one can readily appreciate the superstition that still clings to these insects from days when larger houses were mainly constructed of wood. To hear a Death-watch knocking was thought to be a sure presage of death; nowadays we regard it merely as a sign of structural trouble.

A similar awe, if on a slightly lower plane, is inspired by the activities of the little insect commonly called the Lesser Death-watch, although it is no relation to *Xestobium* and is in fact a book-louse (Order Psocoptera). *Trogium pulsatorium*, for example, is one of several species which lives in old books and under wall-paper, where it feeds on gum bindings, paste and moulds. It signals by rapping its abdomen rhythmically against the surface on which it rests. Being scarcely more than a couple of millimetres long, the insect's efforts are heard only as a faint watch-like ticking, quite unlike the stronger tappings of the beetle, but nevertheless remarkable enough for such a diminutive creature.

Since there are nearly always exceptions to the rule in entomology, it is not surprising to find that some species of the Orthoptera are quite silent, and for one the production of sound involves outside assistance. Lacking means of stridulation, the little Oak bush cricket (*Meconema thalassinum*), which commonly flies into lighted rooms in late summer, drums on a leaf with its forefeet, producing a faint but distinct pattering. The result is softer than the efforts of other crickets and grasshoppers, yet it seems to have the desired effect of attracting the opposite sex.

Still more insect sounds are purely incidental to some other activity, and presumably without special significance, such as the faint 'plick' one hears when a little Skipjack or Click beetle attempts to right itself after having fallen from its perch onto its back. It is caused by a backwardly directed spur on the first part of the thorax being driven forcibly into a cavity on the next, this having the effect of propelling the insect several inches into the air. The insect will continue to jump and click until eventually it falls right side up. Since the beetle will also go through the motions

Mating Bloody-nosed beetles (*Timarcha tenebricosa*). About actual size. Species derives its name from an ability to discharge a blood-coloured fluid from the mouth, presumably as predator repellent.

when held between thumb and forefinger, it is possible that the click, which is mechanical in nature, has a startling effect on predators—while of course the jump itself may put distance between itself and the aggressor.

There are probably many other such insect sounds to be heard, some of them as yet undocumented. Indeed, the topic is a truly fascinating one that would repay further investigation, for it is likely that the insect world is a noisier one than many of us think.

5

NIGHT LIFE

I have never been sure if the poet Thomas Gray was referring to the Cockchafer—commonly but erroneously called May Bug—or one of the shiny black Dor beetles (*Geotrupes*) when he wrote in his famous *Elegy* of the beetle 'wheeling his droning flight' after dark. Whichever it was, and I suppose there are several other possible alternatives as well, most of us have seen flying beetles of one kind or another when out of doors on a fine summer's evening. I myself have more than once narrowly avoided head-on collision with one of these beetle aeronauts as they sped on their way to tree top or dung heap.

Nocturnal activity is typical of a great many insects, not just beetles. Provided the ambient temperature is high enough, and there is little or no wind or rain, some of them are habitually on the move during the late evening and often well into the early hours of the next morning. When daylight comes, they go into hiding again, giving place to the 'day-shift' of sun-loving species. Much of this night-time busy-ness is directly concerned with the twin, and equally vital, objectives of reproduction and feeding; the insects seem to have learned (one uses the word advisedly of course) that they are less prone to attack from predators after dark, although they may still have to run the gauntlet of such night creatures as owls, nightjars and bats.

By far the most familiar, if not the commonest, night-flying insects are moths; indeed most of Britain's 2,000 or so species are nocturnal. To a large extent we come across them by chance because many of them are normally inconspicuous. At night their activities are shrouded in darkness, while during the day, when most of them are at rest, their cryptic coloration enables many species to shade into their surroundings. Some, however, are more extrovert in appearance and habits. Walk through a lush meadow on a June evening, for example, and you will often see male Ghost moths (*Hepialus humuli*) zig-zagging slowly from side to side just above the grass bents, as if held on a puppeteer's string. Their forewings are of the purest white, which makes them easy to see if not to capture. The female Ghost, object of the male's exploratory hoverings, is considerably more elusive and retiring. Spending most of her time clinging to a grass stem, she moves only when attracted by her partner's appearance overhead, and then she flutters up to meet him halfway. Her wings are patterned in dull yellow and reddish brown, which may seem gaudy enough but she is difficult to see after dark when all colours are neutralized.

Such sexual differences in colour are common in the insect world; they often led naturalists in the past to label sexes as distinct species before greater study enabled such errors to be corrected. Many insects also display sexual dimorphism—differences in physical structure, related to specialisation in one particular activity. In the moth world, this is exemplified by the little Winter moth (*Operophtera brumata*), well known as a pest of fruit trees, which somewhat unusually flies on quite cold autumn and winter evenings. The females are totally flightless—mere egg-laying machines—whereas the delicate little males are commonly to be seen on nights from October to January fluttering around street lamps, which divert them from their main function of fertilising the females.

The tendency of many night-flying insects, especially moths, to respond to the lure of artificial light brings us back to the point made earlier about our familiarity with them being largely accidental, for otherwise comparatively few would ever come to our notice. Early naturalists marvelled at the way a moth or other insect would frequently fly so close to a candle or lamp as to burn its wings, but nowadays the attraction is infinitely more significant to insect life. Every summer millions of moths and other night-flying insects are attracted to the lights of houses, factories and other illuminated buildings, as well as street lamps and car head-lights, and many of them die as a result. One motorist actually went to the length of counting the number of moths which spattered themselves over his windscreen over the period of an hour: the final figure was well above a hundred which, considered in a wider context, gives some inkling of the carnage that must take place every summer.

There is evidence to show that street lamps, particularly those of the mercury-vapour type, have drastically reduced the insect populations of many areas. Again I am thinking mainly of moths, for little research seems to have been done on the other kinds of insects which find such lights an irresistible attraction, although in my experience the list is an impressive one. Many of those insects which can fly and are active at night are attracted, from little green lacewings and beetles to crane-flies, caddis-flies, Hymenoptera of many kinds, and a host of others besides. Male glow-worms fre-quently arrive, and so does the impressively antlered male Stag beetle (*Lucanus cervus*), notably in parts of Surrey and Hampshire. One wonders indeed just how many times this noble and decreasing species, which is legally protected in Germany and formed the subject of one of Dürer's finest drawings, has been crushed under-foot by passing pedestrians. Actions of this sort are not entirely involuntary, sad to say. It is hardly likely, for example, that the incident, recently recorded in an entomological magazine, of a motorist deliberately going out of his way to run over a Stag beetle crossing the road was an isolated one. Those who display concern for and interest in insects attracted to street lamps need to prepare

Emperor moths (*Saturnia pavonia*). The two upper moths are females, the lower one, with more distinctively branched antennae, a male. Male emperors are active day-flyers seeking out the sedentary females over moor-lands and similar open areas. Enlarged. (*G. E. Hyde*)

themselves for a certain amount of ridicule—or worse. A few years ago, for example, a man narrowly escaped arrest for drunkenness whilst studying moths in these circumstances; but then perhaps he was lucky to avoid even more serious suspicion after explaining his activity!

But if the average man or woman in the street tends to regard the activities of the insect-student with amusement, many entomologists themselves are beginning to question, seriously, the increasing use of specially designed light-traps for attracting insects in large numbers. The most effective trap is of the mercury-vapour type, giving off a faintly bluish light. This is only moderately perceptible to the human eye but very alluring to insects because the light has a wavelength to which their eyes are sensitive. Personally, I have long doubted the wisdom of using these lamps excessively because they surely intensify the already serious effects of purely utilitarian lights.

Already some species turn up in traps much less frequently than they did and, if the moth-trap trend continues, how long will it be before certain 'fringe' species are reduced to rarity status or even made extinct? This is no flight of fancy. Even if the trapped moths are not killed, but simply recorded and counted, or a few taken for a collection, their subsequent release is likely to be fraught with hazard for the insects. However carefully they are released in grass or undergrowth, their position is rarely one they would choose for themselves, and the effects of the light are frequently so bemusing as to hamper the moths' movements for some considerable time afterwards: in other words, they do not immediately fly away after release. The result must frequently be that much of the catch is quickly disposed of by wandering predators, who find the insects relatively easy to capture.

Apart from all this, artificial light seems to override the most basic functions of feeding and, even more important, of mating and egg-laying. I frequently came across striking examples of this fact during a study of the moths attracted to the neon lights of a local hospital boiler-house. A significant proportion of the moths were females, and many of them were gravid (egg-laden) and automatically deposited their fertile progeny directly after they had been attracted and had settled down. Moths do not normally lay unless and until they have selected the appropriate food plant for their offspring.

Obviously, the tendency to lay automatically can be advantageous to the entomologist who wishes to rear a particular species—for example, I once raised the scarce Emperor and Lappet moths from ova laid by light-attracted females—but it is scarcely an advantage to the moths themselves. Think how many of them must arrive at artificial lights all over the country every summer and deposit eggs whose larvae, far from their food plants, are doomed to starve. We may be able to do little about the effects of purely utilitarian lights (who would listen anyway?), but entomologists could exercise more restraint over deliberate moth-trapping.

The reasons *why* moths find artificial light so alluring are interesting, for on the face of it it seems curious that insects should be so hell-bent on self-destruction. Of course no conscious decision is involved; the insects come because they have to, and are doubtless as puzzled to find themselves diverted from their true goal as anyone watching. Normally it seems that moths and other night-flying insects use celestial bodies such as the moon and stars for navigation and to orientate themselves. By keeping the eye at a constant angle with the light source, they are able to fly on an even keel whilst using their chemotactile-sensitive antennae to find food, larval food plant or partner. Ants and other diurnal insects use the position of the sun in a similar manner. A more local light however, such as a light trap or uncurtained window, will divert an insect and force it to fly directly towards it. Once having arrived at the light source, an insect may try to circle it, attempting to keep at a constant angle with each radiating light ray. In the end it is liable to spiral right into the light, spin off at a tangent or fall to the ground blinded and stunned.

Where a lot of lights are near each other—a mass of town or city lights for example—the final attraction is less marked, pre-

Golden-Y moth (*Plusia jota*). Actual size.

sumably because the effect is that of daylight and the insects instinctively shun such areas, just as they avoid flying during the day. A single light, or isolated group of them, is infinitely more alluring, although a lot depends on the position of the light source, its power in relation to size, and not least where the insect happens to be when it is first affected by the light.

Fortunately, there is another means of deliberately attracting moths and other night-flying insects which is far less drastic in its ultimate effects. The entomologist takes advantage of the insects' 'sweet tooth' by providing a tasty meal which keeps them placid while he examines and identifies them. Lepidopterists have used this so-called 'sugaring' method, mainly with a view to collecting, for centuries. Their recipes have doubtless varied from time to time, depending on the availability of ingredients, but a standard concoction, hallowed by tradition, consists of a quantity of stale beer (a friendly publican could probably help here), some black treacle and brown sugar, plus a few drops of rum or essence of peardrops (amylacetate) to give it an added bouquet. Having prepared this heady brew, which might have prompted Mr Squeers to exclaim 'Here's richness!' with rather more justification than when he hailed his watered-down milk, you then paint some of it at about nose-height on tree boles, posts, garden fences and such like, and await results.

On still, warm nights, the lure of the sugar is often remarkable, particularly on trees along a woodland edge or ride. One will not get the phenomenal results that regularly come from light-trapping, mainly because sugaring is a less powerful diversion for the insects from mating and egg-laying; but therein lies its superior charm. There is no romance in light-trapping. If there are moths in the area, they'll come: they have no choice in the matter. Sugaring involves a much greater element of chance: one never quite knows what is going to turn up. It is possible for example to spend much of the evening attracting nothing more exciting than a host of drably tinted Dark Arches (*Apamea monoglypha*) or other sombre Noctuids, and then, suddenly, like a prince amid paupers, there is a superb Merveille-du-Jour (*Griposia aprilina*), with lichen-like green and black forewings, a gorgeous Red Underwing (*Catocala nupta*), or a delicately marked Peach Blossom (*Thyatira batis*) to make the venture worthwhile.

Peach Blossom moth (*Thyatira batis*). Actual size.

Another point about sugaring, contrasting so strongly with light-trapping, is its very naturalness. The sugar is simply a substitute for nectar. It has no drastic side-effects, as light attraction has. Admittedly, the insects sometimes drink themselves silly and stagger away to revolve in little circles like clockwork planes gone wrong, or fall to the ground in an advanced state of inebriation, and some of these may be caught off-guard by wandering ground predators if they do not quickly recover. Toads, for example, have been known to take advantage of the entomologist's sugar in this way, more especially if the same tree or other sugaring position is used on many consecutive evenings. But then birds and bats are likely to cash in to far greater effect near a light-trap or other light source.

Normally, of course, moths obtain their nectar from flowers as well as the honey-dew deposited by aphides on leaves. In fact it is well worth looking around a garden on warm nights to see what insects are attracted to the more strongly-scented flowers. *Nicotiana* (tobacco plant) is particularly attractive to hawk-moths, which use their extraordinarily long proboscis to penetrate the narrow corolla tube. This apart, a torch is likely to reveal a wealth of various

61

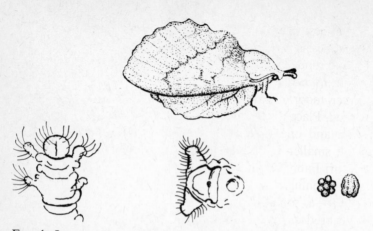

Female Lappet moth (*Gastropacha quercifolia*). (*Below*) Sketches of Lappet moth caterpillar (*Gastropacha quercifolia*) showing the 'lappets', which give the species its common name, and tail claspers. Also, the curious symmetry of the caterpillar's frass (droppings). All about actual size.

insects on vegetation generally, including species one would be unlikely to encounter during daylight.

The ability moths have of picking up scent from a considerable distance during their sexual activities is even more marked—and astonishing—than during food seeking. Almost invariably only the male displays the distant response; the object of his affections simply waits upon his arrival. The antennae of male moths generally are more branched, pectinated or 'feathered' than those of the females, and enable their owners to pick up their future partner's peculiar scent. Nor is the scent put forth by the female simply any odour in the generally accepted sense of the word: it is a deliberately produced perfume, of a highly individual nature, which zoologists call a *pheromone*. A freshly emerged female moth will begin to 'call' by this means as soon as night falls, quivering her wings in the meantime, perhaps to help spread the scent which comes from a special organ at the tip of her abdomen. On suitable evenings, males will frequently respond in an almost unbelievably spectacular way, sometimes travelling several miles in response to the subtle substance.

One of the best known examples of the attractive power of moth pheromones is afforded by the family Saturnidae, of which there is just one representative in Britain, the handsome, eye-marked Emperor moth (*Saturnia pavonia*), males of which fly by day, more especially over moorlands clad with heather on which the larvae commonly feed. Place a newly emerged female Emperor in a gauze-covered cage, and one is likely to find her quickly visited by a swarm of the smaller but more richly tinted males. (The French naturalist Henri Fabre records what must have been an even more spectacular happening of this sort in the case of the Great Emperor (*Saturnia pyri*)—a southern European relative of our species—which he had bred in his own home.)

A great many insect pheromones—for they are produced by other groups apart from moths—are quite undetectable by the human nose. Others are intense and typical of the species. The female Lappet moth (*Gastropacha quercifolia*), for example, smells to me exactly like charcoal, which is curious because the undersides of the moth's body have precisely the appearance of charred wood.

Sexual scents are not confined to night-flying insects. Many butterflies have their own pheromones, although their odours are emitted by the males as a sexual stimulant, and work only at relatively close quarters. Other insect scents have no sexual significance whatsoever, such as the peculiar goat-like smell emitted by the larva of the Goat moth (*Cossus cossus*), which lives a life of continual darkness within trees like elm, ash and willow, on whose wood it feeds, often for up to four years. It is suggested that strong odours of this type may deter predators; certainly the Goat moth larva must be subjected to many hazards during its long life, from parasitic wasps and woodpeckers for example. However it is a moot point whether predatory insects are put off by a little thing like smell, and in any case it is generally supposed that birds do not have a highly developed sense of smell. One possibility is that the Goat larva's pungent odour serves to warn similar larvae to avoid its tunnels—or let egg-laying moths know that the tree is already occupied.

6

FAIRY LAMPS

Many insects are most active at night, and some even have their own built-in lamps to work by. These remarkable insects—the so-called glow-worms and fireflies—have a worldwide distribution, but sadly only two species occur in Britain, one of which is now extremely rare. The other, *Lampyris noctiluca*, is commoner, if less so than formerly, and may still be seen in suitable localities, where its brilliant green but cold 'fire' can be relied upon to warm the hearts of all but the most entrenched insect-haters. Many a poet and country writer has testified to his aesthetic delight at encountering a colony of these intriguing living lights, even though he may not have appreciated their true nature or that of the light itself.

The greatest misunderstanding of all is inherent in the species' everyday name which implies that it belongs to the class of animals whose value Charles Darwin extolled in his classic *The Formation of Vegetable Mould through the Action of Worms* (1881). In fact, the glow-worm is really a beetle, if certainly a most unusual one. The worm epithet seems likely to have arisen from uninformed contemplation of the female insect—always the most frequently encountered of the sexes, since it is she who does all the sedentary glowing. She is totally wingless, with a long segmented body quite unlike that of the smaller, fully winged male, who is also furnished with a lamp but a much smaller one. Unable to fly, she has to content herself with crawling, which she does, rather laboriously,

by hitching up her tail behind her at every stride. Her progress is
not unlike the gait of a looper-moth caterpillar, and for much the
same reason—the legs being concentrated nearer the head than the
tail. The worm-like image is further emphasised by the female's
rather drab, greyish-brown coloration, which is in such complete
contrast to the brilliant light she is able to emit at will.

The glow-worm is among those many insects which have a 'local'
distribution in Britain. Colonies can be found throughout much
of southern England, the Midlands and North, East Anglia, Wales,
and even Scotland (more particularly the Lowlands), but they are
often widely separated. There are probably various reasons for
this, both natural and induced. The basic one seems to be that the
species is always commonest on calcareous soils. As a result the
heaviest concentration of glow-worms occurs on the chalk of the
North and South Downs, as well as in Dorset, and also to a lesser
extent on the limestone of the Yorkshire wolds. Individual habitat
preferences tend to be exceedingly diverse. Grassy hillsides and
thickets, roadside verges and ditches, hedgerows, river and canal
banks and open woodland glades may all harbour colonies, varying

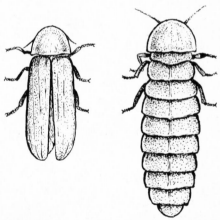

(*left*) Male Glow-worm (*Lampyris noctiluca*). Actual size approx. ½ inch.
(*right*) Female Glow-worm (*Lampyris noctiluca*). Actual size approx. ¾ inch.
Note lack of wings.

from perhaps half a dozen insects to many hundreds. Glow-worms have also been reported from churchyards and gardens, and even on coastal cliffs and beaches, while one of their favourite refuges from the advance of man seems to be railway embankments and cuttings, whether the line is in use or not.

Basically, the habitat is chosen according to the special needs of the larvae rather than those of the adults. Juvenile glow-worms feed almost solely on snails of one sort or another, and since these molluscs are always most plentiful on chalk and limestone, extracting the salts from the soil via their food plants for the essential growth and renewal of their shells, it follows that glow-worms too will be commonest there. Glow-worm larvae take three and sometimes four years to mature and must consume large quantities of snails during this period, but by a curious paradox (which nevertheless occurs among a good many other insects) the adults do not feed at all, and in fact only live for a few weeks, perhaps less if mating takes place promptly after emergence from the pupae.

Human activity has been directly responsible for increasing the distance between many glow-worm colonies. Their basic distributional pattern coincides with areas where man himself is most populous or industrious: inevitably, therefore, many colonies have been, and doubtless still are being, wiped out by land development, the over-liberal use of pesticides, toxic exhaust fumes, close mowing of roadside verges, drainage and so forth. Destruction of habitat is the key factor here, as it is in the depletion of many animal species. It is worth harking back to what was said earlier about the female glow-worm being sedentary in her habits, enforced by a lack of wings. If her traditional territory is destroyed, she and her eggs, laid in the same area, are likely to be destroyed with it. She cannot fly away to try again elsewhere. Males may survive, but this is of little use when the female dictates the species' distribution.

Significantly, because the female glow-worm does not have any wings, the species has never been able to colonise Ireland.

Larvae of Glow-worm (*Lampyris noctiluca*), enlarged about twice and actual size.

At one time, millions of years ago, Britain and Ireland were joined, but then came the last great Ice Age, which covered all of Britain north of the Thames and Severn. During this bleak era, which probably lasted some ten to twenty thousand years, glow-worms (and indeed most insects) would not have been able to survive. With the arrival of a warmer climate, and the gradual retreat of the ice northwards, insects like *Lampyris* would have been able to colonise the southern half of Britain from the then still conjoined mainland of Europe. But it was at this time, too, that the Irish Sea cut in, to form an impassable barrier between the two land masses; the westward movement of glow-worms was halted on the western coasts of Wales and Scotland. The pattern is clear from the distribution map which I have been able to compile over several years, with the help of recorders from all over Britain: a density of population in the south of England, gradually thinning out northwards, but not a single, solitary record from Ireland.

There is another intriguing twist to the glow-worm story which likewise affects its present-day status. One might have thought that this marvellously self-sufficient beetle would ignore man-made light, since it has its own particular brand. But not a bit of it: male glow-worms seem almost as photo-taxic as the moths described in my previous chapter. If colonies occur in gardens, for example, the little males will wing their way into sitting-rooms and bedrooms instead of dutifully seeking out the females whose light is specifically designed as a sexual attractant. Some observers have reported

A female Glow-worm (*Lampyris noctiluca*) posed on its back by the photographer to show the three bands of luminescent material at the end of the abdomen. Female Glow-worms are quite wingless, whereas the male is fully winged with much larger and prominent eyes especially designed to discern the female's light.

(Robin Fletcher)

glow-worms actually making their way into beds, and one lady had the charming experience of finding a glow-worm on her daughter's pillow, displaying its pinpoints of light beside the girl's billowing hair. Others have discovered them beneath the sheets, producing an initially mystifying circle of light. Insect light-orientation is remarkable enough, but it seems doubly strange that the highly specialised attraction of the female glow-worm's light can be so readily overridden for the male by artificial illuminants.

While there cannot be much doubt that *Lampyris* is considerably less common in Britain than it was, say, twenty or thirty years ago, for the reasons mentioned, our decreasing familiarity with this delightful insect may not be simply because of its numerical decline; it could also be partly due to man's own changing social habits. Several of my correspondents have made the valid point that we ourselves are no longer the pedestrian, semi-nocturnal animals we once were, so that our chances of seeing glow-worms have become fewer. With the advent of the motor car, the country-man's shorter working hours, and counter-attractions like TV, the average person is less often out and about on foot after dark in the countryside. Even the courting couple are more likely to take the car than wander slowly down some leafy-bowered lane and point out a glow-worm as their fallen star. Drivers in general are unlikely to see glow-worms' fairy twinklings as they speed by. In consequence, most reports of glow-worms, outside gardens and such like, tend to come from committed naturalists, such as the nocturnal moth-trapper or the nightjar and nightingale listener.

We must not forget, too, that the season during which glow-worms display their light is relatively short and easily missed. Like many insects, the adults live only just long enough to ensure the perpetuation of the species, so that if the females succeed in attracting a mate quickly, egg-laying and death of the parents follow rapidly. Then again the weather conditions have to be right. A chilly night will almost certainly inhibit glowing or the emergence of the adults from the pupae; so too will wind and rain, although thundery, humid conditions may prove more fruitful, particularly if the temperature remains high just after a storm. These factors together make it easy to overlook a colony in any one season, or perhaps to see just one or two individuals, or even none at all. A report to the effect that a colony has either declined or disappeared may indicate only that the observer has simply not been present at the right time.

If you are fortunate enough to find a glow-worm colony, you need not confine your study to the adults. Careful examination of a known habitat could reveal the eggs, perhaps affixed to grass stems or nestling in moss. They are spherical in shape and very small, scarcely more than a millimetre in diameter, and of a rich yellow tint. Seeking them during the daytime would be very much like trying to find the proverbial needle; but there is no need. You have a better chance after dark because, to add wonder upon wonder, the eggs also glow with a strange inner light, reminiscent of the adults, but yellower. Even the larvae and pupae glow, both having twin pinpoints of light at the tip of the abdomen. Some consider such pre-imaginal light to have a defensive value. Certainly both larvae and pupae will react by glowing if one acts the part of a predator and breathes strongly upon them.

It is doubtful if the response deters all aggressors, however. Toads, for example, have been known to snap up glow-worms, completely indifferent to their built-in beacons. More recently, one of my correspondents provides strong circumstantial evidence of bats taking glow-worms, swooping down to pick them off grass stems. This can be explained by the fact that bats have a weak appreciation of light and their vision generally is poor. Presumably their exceedingly sensitive hearing helps them to locate their prey with such precision.

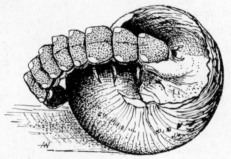

Larval Glow-worm attacking snail. Enlarged × 2 approx. Note different shape of thoracic segment behind head and white spots at corner of each body segment, distinguishing the larva from the adult female.

Larval glow-worms tend to be slightly more overt in their habits than the adults, emerging after hibernation in spring to seek food and perhaps absorb the warmth of the sun. They feed, however, mostly after dark or at least out of sight, and one needs to be a particularly assiduous observer to watch them doing so. Many kinds of snails are eaten, including young garden snails (*Helix aspersa*), banded snails (*Cepaea* spp), the small *Hygromia striolata*, species of the flattish *Oxychilus* genus, and doubtless many others. One or two people have told me of larvae feeding on slugs, but one questions whether they commonly do so in a wild state, simply because of the way they feed. As with many larval insects, feeding involves a kind of external digestion. The larva injects its victim with a special enzyme which first paralyses the snail and then breaks down its tissue into a broth-like consistency. The larva then drinks this through its hollow mandibles.

The snail's shell makes a convenient receptacle for the liquefied substance, whereas a slug of course cannot be so easily contained. It spreads in a glutinous mass, so that smaller glow-worm larvae feeding on it are in constant danger of sharing the Duke of Clarence's fate, drowning in a sea of nutriment—as in fact actually happened to some larvae I reared in captivity. What is intriguing is that a single larva will sometimes overcome a fairly large snail and allow the prey to be shared by others. I have several times seen groups of my home-reared larvae ranged round the lip of the shell of liquefied snail, feeding communally, reminding one of nothing so much as piglets at a trough. It makes one wonder in fact if there is any truth in the contention that the larval light is a means of encouraging and concentrating larval feeding of this sort; it would doubtless be useful if snails were scarce.

As Fabre has described so graphically, after each meal a glow-worm larva is able to give itself a good wash and brush up, to remove the traces of snail tissue with which it is often liberally smeared after having ventured right inside the shell to remove the last vestiges. Cleaning is not done with its legs or mouthparts but with a special forked device, white in colour and soft and sticky in consistency, which is extruded from the tail end. Curling this portable brush about itself, the larva systematically sponges off the snail slime until it is clean again. Since adult glow-worms do not predate, they lack this appendage.

One must ask how the glow-worm's light is produced. In principle it is a biochemical reaction, involving the breakdown of a certain substance to release energy in the form of light. The light-producing material is visible on the underside of the female glow-worm's abdomen, the last three segments of which are slightly yellowish white. This glowing area consists of a substance called luciferin which glows when oxygen passes on to it from tubes within the insect's body, together with a special enzyme or catalyst called luciferase. At the back of the luciferin is a layer of reflecting crystals which act like a mirror in diverting all the light outwards, so that none is lost. Precisely how the glow-worm is able to replenish the luciferin is not known; in fact it seems almost self-renewing. It is also remarkably efficient. No heat loss is involved; practically all the energy is given out as light. This is far from being the case with even the most sophisticated forms of man-made illumination. Low-pressure fluorescence, for example, is only 60 per cent efficient; much of its energy is converted into heat, and the ordinary tungsten-filament light bulb becomes so hot that it cannot be handled at all after only a short period of illumination.

In view of this, some might ask why man has not thought of harnessing glow-worm and firefly light for his own use. There are several reasons. First, manufacturing luciferin artificially seems both difficult and costly; while it would obviously be impractical to try to use the insects' own material—the number of glow-worms needing to be sacrificed would be colossal! But the main factor is the nature of the light itself. It seems unlikely, to say the least, that people would take kindly to living part of their days in an all-greenish aura; for one thing, it would tend to make certain colours invisible.

At a more modest level, of course, live glow-worms can certainly be used as a stop-gap illuminant. We in Britain would probably not go to the lengths of confining them in special containers to read by, as poor Chinese and Japanese students are said to have done at one time, but more than one of us has tried the experiment of reading his paper or looking at a watch with their aid. Some have shown much greater imagination, like the man who hit upon the idea of replacing a spent bicycle headlight bulb with a number of glow-worms. Unfortunately, as someone should have told him, the insects have a disconcerting way of dousing their lights from time to time, and this happened just as our hero encountered the local bobby!

Distinctive and unmistakable as glow-worm light is to those who are familiar with it, there are nevertheless a number of other natural phenomena with which it might conceivably be confused. Earlier on, we mentioned the fact that there is another, much rarer, species of glow-worm to be found in this country. *Phosphaenus hemipterus* is like *Lampyris noctiluca* in most respects, but the male has shorter elytra or wing-covers and the female's light-producing area is confined to the last two segments of the abdomen, not three as in *Lampyris*. Since there are definite records of *Phosphaenus* only from certain parts of Sussex, and those with one exception not recent, the chances of seeing the species are in any case regrettably slim. Some people are occasionally misled into mistaking as glow-worms some of the very thin Geophilid centipedes which live in soil and leaf litter and can emit a whitish incandescence by some method which is not entirely clear. E. H. Eason, in his *Centipedes of the British Isles* (Warne 1964), tells us that one species, *Geophilus carpophagus*, is actually known as 'glow-worm' in some parts of the country—which doesn't help! The light is, however, of a different character from the true glow-worm's, while if one is able to examine the source closely it will be seen to emanate from the whole length of the centipede's body, not just the tip. A number of fungi are also luminous under certain conditions, but since these are hardly likely to retreat from the observer he is not likely to mistake their identity!

7

EARWIGS IN MY BED

Many people who dislike insects might be prepared to tolerate them if they did not display a tendency, even at times a positive determination, to make their way indoors. It is surprising how so many different species assume the role of squatters, especially in old buildings with plenty of dark nooks and crannies. Some indeed are likely to have been there for generations, far longer than the human occupants—which ought theoretically to confer on them some sort of legal status!

Of the three main categories of insect guests—true residents, hibernators, and casual visitors—the first are perhaps the most interesting, mainly because some of them have become such confirmed commensals of man that they are now found scarcely anywhere else. One of these includes a species which is probably among the most heartily loathed of all the insect tribe. The Common Cockroach (*Blatta orientalis*), commonly but quite erroneously called the 'black beetle' on account of its shiny blackish-brown coloration and superficially beetle-like appearance, represents the very epitome of insect horror for those unable to take a more objective view.

Cosmopolitan in its distribution, here is a species which must have lived close to man ever since he first began to seek shelter in caves or mud huts, since it is a confirmed scavenger and thrives on all kinds of human detritus. Although somewhat less common nowadays, this scuttling, long-feelered, 'long-legged beastie' is still one of the causes of those subdued scratchings and rustlings which alarm the insomniac in the wee small hours, eliciting a shriek from the woman of the house who may step on one while seeking a glass of water in the kitchen. But at least we may comfort ourselves with the knowledge that cockroaches mean us no personal harm. Their nocturnal wanderings are almost entirely geared towards a search for food scraps. Being very flat-bodied, they are able to make their home in the cracks at the base of a wall or beneath a skirting board, and unless steps are taken to remove them, they will breed and thrive in such situations, producing their eggs in little purse-like capsules or *ootheca*.

Several other species of cockroach live in houses or other buildings in Britain, but all of them are recent aliens and none is as common as *Blatta orientalis*. As its scientific name suggests, our common species is also a foreigner, although it has been here so long as to have become English by adoption, as it were. It is supposed to have been accidentally introduced via trading vessels from the Middle East; just when is in doubt. Gilbert White records *Blatta* as being a newcomer at Selborne around the 1780s, but it had probably established itself here long before that, especially around the coasts.

A less daunting competitor for such food scraps as we may neglect to clear away is equally shy of showing itself in daytime but nevertheless broadcasts its presence in a totally unmistakable way. Like cockroaches, the little House cricket (*Acheta domesticus*) takes advantage of suitable crevices or hidden corners about the house, especially by an open fire or behind a radiator; the more fastidious may feel obliged to oust it, perhaps by leaving a jar of sour milk on the floor—allegedly an infallible trap. Others feel differently. Indeed, there is a long tradition of tolerance of this little fireside singer, partly on account of its cheerful song, which may be produced both by day and night, but also because it is said to vary its scavenging diet by attacking and killing cockroaches: a distinct point in its favour!

There is an age-old belief that a cricket in the house will bring good fortune to its human occupants—a conviction shared by Charles Dickens's character Mrs Perrybingle. In his charming novel *The Cricket on the Hearth*, Dickens recounts how the Peerybingles' cricket would vie with and even outdo the whistle of the kettle boiling merrily on the kitchen fire, perhaps taking it for a rival: I have a distinct recollection of something similar happening in the ancient cottage where I lived as a child.

House crickets are less prolific breeders than cockroaches but, like them, will stay indoors all the year round if conditions are right. They are not totally housebound, however, for there are many records of their taking up residence on council rubbish tips; indeed, I know of a colony on a tip not more than a mile from my home. In outdoor situations the adults seem to hibernate regularly in sheltered positions.

Many of the insect residents of the house are, like the cricket and cockroach, creatures of darkness, emerging only at night to forage and feed. Others are slightly more extrovert, but their small size and ability to make use of the very smallest retreats, such as cracks in the plaster or behind wallpaper or furniture, means that they are commonly overlooked. One of these, the primitive Silverfish (*Lepisma saccharina*) is probably far commoner indoors than the fastidious, anti-insect housewife imagines. Never more than half an inch long, but with very long antennae and (three) tail filaments, Silverfish are covered with minute silvery scales which stick to the finger if you are quick enough to intercept their sinuous, vaguely fish-like dashes over wall or brickwork. You will find them in all sizes, however, for *Lepisma* undergoes no proper metamorphosis, or larval development, the little nymphs simply getting larger after each successive skin-change. The worst that can be said against these tiny insects is that they occasionally feed on the gum bindings of books and the paste used to stick wallpaper to the wall; for the most part they scavenge on minute food particles as well as dead insects.

Of the less benevolently inclined denizens long associated with human dwellings, a good many have become far less common in

76

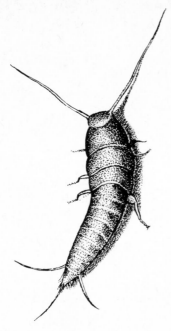

Silverfish (*Lepisma saccharina*): a
common inhabitant of houses. Greatly
enlarged; actual size approx. ½ inch.

these days of increased hygiene. One such is the Bed bug (*Cimex lectularius*), although it is far from being totally eradicated. Even the most fervent, single-minded entomologist would hardly admit to housing a colony of these blood-sucking Heteropterids, but the prospect of an infestation is not entirely remote, particularly if secondhand bedding is used or stored. Obviously, scrupulous cleanliness helps to deter them; on the other hand a modern centrally-heated house is likely to be more attractive to them than a traditionally warmed one since it enables them to breed faster.

Bed bugs are fortunately large enough to be easily seen with the naked eye, being about a quarter of an inch long, with an almost circular if rather flat abdomen; when gorged with blood they become fatter and reddish in colour. But they and their young can survive without feeding for long periods. As a result they might well be lurking in old mattresses and bedding, cracks in the walls and furniture, just waiting to pounce on the hapless sleeper. While some people display an allergic reaction when bitten by Bed bugs, usually the effect is only a mild, temporary irritation, and the bug does not seem to transmit any disease in Britain. *Cimex lectularius* is another immigrant it seems, for there are no records of its presence here until the early sixteenth century, when it was still uncommon.

In Chapter 4 we mentioned a species of louse which sometimes occurs indoors: the Book louse, *Trogium pulsatorium*, whose faint tappings may sometimes be heard from within the leaves of old damp books and wood. The lice that afflict our bodies belong to a different order, *Anoplura*. *Pediculus humaniscapitis*, for example, feeds on the scalp and hair follicles, while there are also body and crab lice, the last-mentioned showing a preference for pubic hair, although eyebrows too are frequently singled out for attention. Several such species are far from being mere irritants. Some carry typhus, which explains why, during the last war, when there was a great mix of evacuees from London and other cities, we village children had our heads regularly examined for 'nits', as the larvae of head lice are called.

Even to read about man-biting parasites makes many of us itch, so it is perhaps a relief to turn to some of the insects which ignore us personally but find our possessions attractive. The activities of the Furniture beetle (*Anobium punctatum*) are often extremely insidious, and frequently the first signs we see of their presence are little piles of sawdust beneath furniture, or the adult beetles wandering about a window in spring. If the beetles are crushed they will often be found to contain masses of tiny white eggs, since mating commonly takes place outside their larval tunnellings, whereas actual egg-laying occurs both inside and on the surface of the wood.

While Furniture beetles attack only old well-seasoned wood, there are other beetles which do the reverse. If you have just moved into a new house, or had a timber-framed extension added, a much larger, long-horned beetle larva could be chewing its way through

78

the woodwork, all unknown to you. Without wishing to be alarmist, since these larvae sometimes spend several years in timber, and are not invariably killed when it is cut up and prepared for sale, it is likely that any adults seen wandering about do come from such tunnellings, which are depressingly large in size.

Sometimes, too, building timber is infested by large wood wasps of the genera *Sirex* and *Uroceras*, the one black and dull yellow, the other metallic purple-blue. However, these species are also occasionally attracted to artificial light, so there is no need to jump to conclusions too soon. Yet another Hymenopterid is a parasite on wood wasps, thrusting its needle-like ovipositor through the outer bark to reach the larvae. The adult *Rhyssa persuasoria* has a much slimmer body than either *Sirex* or *Uroceras*, and is black, banded with greenish-yellow. The larval *Rhyssa* does not itself feed on wood, but draws its nourishment from its host, whose tissues it sucks until the completion of its development, which presumably takes far less time than the two to three years needed by the wood wasp itself.

The kitchen-window ornithologist may be surprised to learn that his or her tolerance of sparrows' nests in the guttering, or more particularly house-martins' nests under the eaves, is likely to produce unexpected results in the form of tiny beetle larvae of the Dermestidae family. In the normal way, species like the Larder beetle (*Dermestes lardarius*) and Carpet beetle (*Anthrenus verbasci*) lay their eggs in such nests, the larvae feeding on the feather and hair linings. Not infrequently, however, the little hairy, dark-banded grubs insinuate themselves through windows and up overflow pipes to end up chewing the carpet or other fabrics.

Another closely related species, the Museum beetle (*Anthrenus museorum*), has a particularly bad reputation because of its unsporting tendency to consume museum specimens (as also, incidentally, do wasps). Birds' nests may also be the primary source of visits from the curious little Spider beetles, so-called because of their long legs, round thorax and head; none is more than about three or four millimetres long, but one, the Golden Spider beetle (*Niptus holoceurus*), is of a particularly distinctive appearance, having a golden pubescence. Clothes moths, too, may intrude from birds' nests. Indeed, it seems likely that nests and similar places were the main habitats of these tiny moths before man began to wear animal skins and woollens and take up a settled existence.

One cannot write about domestic entomology without mentioning the Earwig (*Forficula auricularia*), probably second only to the Common Cockroach in terms of human unpopularity. These maligned insects are inveterate climbers and insist on inviting themselves indoors from time to time, to the dismay of many who believe they may end up in his or her ear. The ear-piercing idea is absurd, of course, though an earwig could presumably *enter* an ear: it would be unlikely to stay long or do any damage while there. In defence of earwigs, I am convinced that they are largely scavengers by nature. If you find them feeding, outdoors or indoors, it is almost always on minute, often unidentifiable scraps. I did once watch an earwig in the bath consume a dead fly completely, and even on one memorable occasion a fragment of red soap! Those who like to anthropomorphize ought perhaps to admire earwigs, for they display a pronounced maternal instinct and solicitousness for their young, in sharp contrast to most of the class.

If the majority of householders view the insect residents mentioned so far with a somewhat jaundiced eye, probably few of us object to the presence of a hibernating Small Tortoiseshell butterfly (*Aglais urticae*) or an eyed-wing Peacock (*Nymphalis io*). Both of these attractive species spend the winter in adult form, and at the first threat of colder weather may seek a dark corner indoors in

 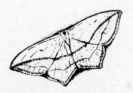

(*left*) Barred Yellow moth (*Cidaria fulvata*). Actual size.
(*right*) Blood-vein moth (*Calothysanis amata*). About actual size.

80

which to sleep. During this period of inactivity, their rate of respiration is exceedingly low, so that they use up very little energy and can survive without feeding. Unfortunately, the butterflies have a tendency to awake on some unseasonably sunny winter's day and flutter vainly in the window, usually ending up as sad corpses on the floor. It is of course useless to release them; there would be unlikely to be any natural food about, and even if they found a mate and produced eggs the resultant larvae would almost certainly die from lack of sustenance or the cold.

You can however do something to extend the lives of awakened hibernating butterflies by feeding them, forcibly if necessary, on a dilute sugar solution—perhaps a little syrup dissolved in warm water. The insects may drink what is put before them without further ado, particularly if their forefeet, with which they are able to 'taste', touch the liquid; but if they do not feed immediately it is possible to uncoil the watch-spring-like proboscis with a pin and dip it into the liquid, while holding the insect gently but firmly by the wings just above the thorax. The butterfly should then be put back in some shaded corner, although not one where it is likely to find itself imprisoned and forgotten when spring comes round!

Peacocks and Small Tortoiseshells are the most usual butterfly hibernators indoors. Some people tell of finding the large Red Admiral (*Vanessa atalanta*) in a dormant state, though I have never done so myself. Normally, it seems, the adults die off in the autumn and are replenished by immigrations from the Continent and North Africa in the following summer. One might even, with extreme luck, be favoured by the rare Camberwell Beauty (*Nymphalis antiopa*) as a winter guest, since these regal visitors from Scandinavia will not survive our winters unless they find a suitable place in which to hibernate. A lady a few miles from my village found one sheltering in a woodpile gathered for the November 5th village bonfire, which suggests the species has not yet become accustomed to seeking out homely British hospitality.

Butterflies are of course far from being the only insects that hibernate, or seek to do so, in our houses. Some of the pretty green

81

Emerald moths do so, and also the sturdier and highly distinctive Herald (*Scoliopteryx libatrix*), whose scalloped-edged forewings are decorated with patches of fiery orange. Ladybirds, mostly of the two- or seven-spot species, lurk in corners and are often awakened by sunshine or the warmth of the room, while little tinsel-winged Lacewings (*Chrysopa carnea*) are also regularly found indoors during the winter. A large number of insects over-winter as eggs, larvae or pupae. Relatively few of these are likely to turn up about the house, although if you grow brassicas in a nearby garden plot the caterpillars of Large and Small White butterflies (*Pieris brassicae* and *P. rapae*) may be found crawling up walls, or even wandering indoors, in order to pupate. Many of these, especially the larvae of the Large White, are attacked by tiny Braconid wasps which lay their eggs in the caterpillars' tissues, the effect being to prevent pupation; so instead of a chrysalis attached to the wall you may find a dead larval skin and a mass of tiny cylindrical yellow silken cocoons attached to it.

The tendency of many insects to be attracted to artificial light has already been discussed in Chapter 5. This is often disconcerting to the lady of the house who may feel that the moths are hell-bent on entangling themselves in her hair, when they are doubtless as puzzled to be there as she is to see them. They are well worth a closer look, however, should they settle or if the observer can secure them. A brilliantly-lit room, more especially one overlooking a meadow or woodland, is likely to attract a wide range of different species, particularly in June and July when the greatest variety, or at least those most commonly attracted, are on the wing. Big brown Drinker moths (*Philudoria potatoria*) or Poplar hawks (*Laothoe populi*) may zoom around the light-shade like miniature fighter-planes. Another visitor could be the gaudy Garden Tiger (*Arctia caja*), whose fluttering flight contrasts with the subtle

Full-grown caterpillar of an Emperor moth (*Saturnia pavonia*). There is considerable difference in the colour and patterning of this caterpillar's different instars. It feeds on a variety of plants, including bramble, dewberry, sloe, hawthorn (as here) and heather. (*G. E. Hyde*)

83

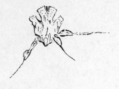

Head-on view of Golden Plusia moth (*Polychrisia moneta*) showing curious tippets. Actual size.

insinuations of tiny wave and pug moths which seem content to settle on the nearest wall.

Because moths have soft bodies, their frequent crashings against a window in high summer are somewhat muted, in contrast to the bullet-like impact of the more heavily armoured Cockchafer beetle, whose arrival could well provoke comment about 'those dratted boys again' if the real culprit is not identified. Calculated to produce a qualm in a different way are the crane-flies or daddy-long-legs, particularly numerous in late summer when they emerge *en masse* from their subterranean pupae, or the orange-bodied

Three views of Poplar Hawk-moth (*Laothoe populi*): head-on, side and above. Actual size.

84

Ophion ichneumon flies which flutter about and occasionally 'ping' against a light bulb. The long ovipositor of the female ichneumon (actually a Hymenopterid and not a true fly) is said to be capable of giving a painful stab if carelessly handled, though probably few will give it the opportunity!

One might think that the Common Housefly (*Musca domestica*) —best-known of all insect denizens of houses—has little to commend it, and scarcely warrants mention here. After all, war needs to be constantly waged against it on account of its habit of pre-digesting its (or rather our) food. Nevertheless, the species can, in my experience, come up with some surprising and fascinating aspects of behaviour. Two examples will I hope demonstrate the point. I met with the first when having swatted a house fly I found a tiny false-scorpion clinging to one of its legs. Now, false-scorpions are not insects but arachnids—relatives of the spiders and of the true scorpion whose shape they so closely resemble. But there was no predation here: the fly was in no danger. The false-scorpion was simply using the fly as a means of transport, taking advantage of its greater mobility to seek pastures new, perhaps more favourable for food and egg-laying. It was one of the few examples of insect hitch-hiking—scientifically known as *phoresy*—that I have ever seen, although such associations also occur in many other kinds of insects.

No less intriguing was the encounter between a fly and a small spider I observed on our kitchen wall. The fly was much too large to be threatened by the spider, and the two faced each other squarely as if weighing each other up. Then, suddenly, the fly advanced upon the spider in short jerky runs and literally buzzed it—retreating and repeating the action several times before the spider seemed to have had enough and made off. I will leave the reader to interpret the reason for such behaviour, for I have no explanation to give, unless it be in the most blatantly anthropomorphic terms; but the episode does I think show that even the most despised insects possess a certain character and interest, and are well worth watching.

85

8

ENTOMOLOGICAL NURSEMAID

When young Jimmy brings home a caterpillar and keeps it in a jar in his bedroom, some parents regard such an interest as simply a childish trait that, hopefully, he will soon grow out of. After all, the harassed housewife has enough trouble coming to terms with the insects that invite themselves without having escape-prone crawlies to contend with. But entomologists, from the ages of seven to seventy, do this sort of thing all the time, as indeed they must if they wish to learn and keep on learning. However much pleasure you gain from simply looking at insects out of doors in their natural habitats, there comes a time when you find some pre-adult form you cannot identify unless you take it home, provide for its needs, and literally see what develops.

Such an approach also has its practical applications to field work. Many times I have discovered larvae which might have left me completely baffled but for the fact that I happened to have bred that particular species in captivity. If the entomologist is leading a field meeting, it boosts his reputation enormously if he is able to say, for example, that the batch of small black and orange-banded caterpillars feeding on dewberry are those of the Emperor moth. He is unlikely to be so confident of his identification without having reared the species, because the full-grown Emperor caterpillar is quite different in appearance: a superb deep velvety green, adorned with gold-studded black bands. Such extreme difference in the appearance of larvae from one instar, or stage

86

between skin changes, to the next is common in the Lepidoptera, and an excellent reason for keeping careful notes, taking photographs or making sketches, since few books illustrate more than the mature caterpillar—if they do that.

The Emperor moth, together with other large species like the Puss and the hawk-moths, are both spectacular in appearance and relatively easy to keep, and therefore the beginner will probably wish to begin his breeding experiments with species like these. Provided they are not overcrowded, the caterpillars will usually reward their captor by feeding steadily and at intervals changing their skin when the old one becomes too tight for comfort. Hawk-moths require a layer of soil in the bottom of their cage, since the larvae pupate underground, but it is probably best to disinter the pupae, after allowing two or three weeks for the change to be completed, and place them on dry, sterile moss or cottonwool in airtight tins, remembering of course to remove the lid nearer the time when the moths are due to emerge. Pupae require little or no air, while the closed atmosphere helps to prevent dessication. It is nevertheless a good idea to open the tins at intervals and sprinkle a few drops of water, or breathe on the pupae a few times, to maintain the moisture level.

Immature larvae of Vapourer moth (*Orgyia antiqua*), first instar (below) and second instar (above). Lower drawing enlarged; above almost actual size.

87

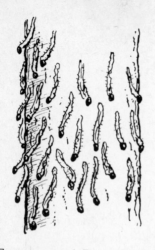

Moulted skins of young Buff-tip moth caterpillars (*Phalera bucephala*). Actual size.

Emperor and Puss moths need no such attention in the pupal stage. The former spin wonderfully intricate and tough bottle-shaped silken cocoons amid their food plant, or perhaps in the corner of the cage. Puss moths go one better by making their superbly disguised cocoons against the bole of the trees whose leaves they eat (mainly willow and sallow), interweaving pieces of bark with their silk. To simulate such a situation, then, you need to provide pieces of bark for the maturing caterpillars to use.

Watching a caterpillar emerge from the egg, change its skin or pupate, or the adult finally struggle forth from the pupa, constitutes the joys of insect rearing. Unfortunately, it all too often happens that one is not on hand at the crucial moment: the thing has happened in your absence. It really depends on how much time you have—and your patience. Skin-changing is particularly fascinating to watch, though it is often an extremely long-drawn out affair. Typically, the caterpillar clings to its perch, to which it anchors itself with a silken pad, its head at a slightly unusual angle and seeming scarcely to belong to the body. This sphinx-like immobility may be maintained for long periods; but keep watching if you can for eventually the skin splits down the centre, the old head is pushed aside, and the new-suited caterpillar wriggles its way out. Sometimes the old head comes adrift quite separately and is flicked off like a discarded hat.

Pupation is less often witnessed, for the simple reason that so many species undergo this change in cocoons underground, or otherwise away from the inquisitive entomologist's eye. It is more easily watched in butterflies which pupate against the sides of their food-plant, although I once had the extreme good fortune to observe the pupation of an Eyed hawk-moth caterpillar which decided to make its pupal chamber right against one side of the glass fish-tank I had provided as its home. I thus had a grandstand view of the whole business: a rare peep behind the curtain which is so often kept closely drawn against the investigator. In this case, of course, the change was more dramatic than a simple shuffling off of an old skin; it involved the total transformation to a relatively inert pupa, which at first was the most beautiful shade of vivid green but gradually darkened to near-black. Just before disappearing underground, when it galloped around the confines of its glass prison at an amazing rate, the caterpillar had assumed all the hectic colours of an autumn leaf, indicating the physiological changes beginning to take place beneath its skin.

However careful he is in nursing his insect charges, the amateur insect breeder must not expect invariable success. Frequently, instead of a perfect butterfly or moth, a parasitic fly or wasp (maybe several of them) struggles forth from the pupal husk; for parasitism of Lepidoptera is far from being confined to those species we might regard as expendable, such as the White butterflies mentioned earlier. Such attacks are part of nature's round. Some of a butterfly's or moth's progeny are almost inevitably going to succumb in this or other ways; indeed it is precisely for this reason that insects always lay large numbers of eggs, so that there is more chance of at least some of them attaining maturity.

Parasitism of this sort may not even be the keeper's fault. The larvae could well have been 'stung' before being collected in the field; some Hymenopterids and Dipterids also parasitize eggs or pupae. On the other hand, livestock is always liable to attack from parasites indoors too, unless steps are taken to prevent access and a careful watch kept for intruders.

It is often difficult to view these insidious attacks by parasites dispassionately, when one's main objective has been cut short so disappointingly. In a way, it is perhaps a test of the entomologist's feeling for his subject as a whole, for really one should regard such insects as being as interesting as the butterfly or moth they have consumed—as indeed they are. That few people take this objective attitude is indicated by the fact that much less is known about the life-histories and host preferences of ichneumon flies, chalcids and other parasites than of other groups; yet they must be more familiar to butterfly and moth breeders, at least by sight, than to anyone else. At least any such examples of parasitization should always be carefully recorded, and the parasites themselves identified, perhaps with the help of specialists such as those at the British Museum (Natural History), who are always ready to give their advice.

I have deliberately made only a brief mention of the techniques of rearing butterflies and moths since there are several excellent books which provide detailed information (see 'Selected Further Reading'). It is a different matter when one turns to other Orders. The literature on them and their life histories is much scantier and more difficult to find, perhaps tucked away in some obscure journal (often in a foreign language), and this in spite of the fact that they vastly outnumber the more showy groups. Even the early stages of many species of Lepidoptera are not fully known, mainly on account of their small size and secretiveness. More than half of the 2,000 or so species of British moths are loosely known as 'micros' (short for *Microlepidoptera*), many of them being extremely minute. Some have curious larval habits like eating within rolled-up leaves or burrowing their way between the upper and lower surfaces of leaves, creating a twisting 'mine' effect which many a countryside rambler must have seen. These groups are well worth studying, and some are extremely beautiful in the adult stage— like the long-antennaed Sun moth (*Nemophora degeerella*) or the

Burnished Brass moth (*Plusia chrysitis*). Actual size.

Crimson-and-Gold (*Pyrausta purpuralis*) whose regally purple, gold-edged forewings make it truly a little gem, especially when just emerged from the pupa. To the true entomologist who is not 100 per cent scientist, small is indeed perfect.

Keeping the early stages of insects like these—always provided one can find them—presents highly individual, though far from insuperable, problems. The difficulty is equally pronounced, in a slightly different way, with the insect groups, such as certain beetles, which spend their larval days feeding in decaying animal or vegetable matter, such as manure or wood, or in the soil. Some beetle larvae are rather easier to keep and observe, such as those of ladybirds, slate-blue in ground-colour with black and yellow spots. These, and the flattish, vaguely slug-like legless larvae of hover-flies, are often to be found on rose bushes afflicted with greenfly, on which they feed despite the attentions of ants who tend the aphides for the sake of their honey-dew. Another aphis-eater is the curious little 'aphis-lion', the larva of the lacewing, which sucks out its victim's internal juices by means of its large sickle-like mandibles. I have frequently brought these tiny insects home quite unknowingly, while collecting leafage for Lepidopterous larvae, and then fed them with aphides offered on the end of a fine camel-hair paintbrush. It was interesting to note that the younger, presumably more tender, aphides were always much preferred!

It is rarely possible to over-feed insect larvae, because eating is their business—their only occupation in fact. With adult insects and other animals it is sometimes a different matter. People who have kept toads commonly report that they will take worms and other fare until you grow tired of trying to satisfy them. Something similar happened with an adult *Feronia madida* ground-beetle

91

I once kept for a short period. It ate so many of the tender white ant pupae I had filched from a nest that its abdomen became greatly distended, displaying the white segment divisions and raising the wing-covers to a most undignified height. In the normal way, one imagines that even this heavily armoured predator would hesitate to raid an ants' nest and risk immolation by the enraged workers, so the beetle is unlikely to have fed on such delicacies before.

Paradoxically, the most widely detested insects are often among the most interesting and rewarding to keep. One such is the Earwig, mentioned in the previous chapter as an occasional infiltrator into the house. In the early part of the year, usually about February or March, you can sometimes find the females crouching over a batch of oval, pearly-white eggs beneath a stone or old log. Like certain shield-bugs (Heteroptera), the mother Earwig is an extremely solicitous parent, constantly licking and turning the eggs to prevent the growth of moulds, and carrying them away one by one in her mouth if their position becomes unsafe. Nor does she abandon her progeny once they have hatched, but feeds and protects them with her body like a hen with a brood of chicks.

It is not difficult to keep both parent and young in a small box or glass tube, covered when not under observation, but care should be taken not to disturb the mother too much or she may become agitated and eat her own offspring, rather as a doe rabbit tends to do if upset. This may also happen if she is given insufficient protein. Freshly killed flies are welcomed, as well as scraps of vegetables, while a few drops of water need to be introduced from time to time, both for drinking and to maintain a slightly moist atmosphere.

Earlier in this chapter I referred to the value of keeping careful notes of the progress made by captive insects. These are not merely useful for personal future reference but are often publishable. Most of the entomological journals will accept short notes or lengthier properly documented articles on insects from the amateur enthusiast. Oldroyd (1970) gives useful hints on how to write up observations, and also lists some of the periodicals worth consulting.

One aspect of insect rearing probably worth touching upon here concerns the butterflies and larger moths, with which I began the chapter, more closely than other Orders. This is the question of the advisability and problems of releasing bred insects into the wild. It is a question that still causes a good deal of controversy in the entomological world, especially in the pages of the specialist journals. I am not thinking of foreign species, since there are many reasons why their release would be inadvisable: one being that their introduction could upset the balance of species already here. (One has only to look at the world of mammals to see what havoc has been caused by the deliberate introduction of foreign species, such as grey squirrel, mink and coypu.) Nor is there any objection to simply returning adult insects to the area from which you collected them as larvae or eggs. The trouble arises particularly with species rare or uncommon in Britain which may have been collected abroad or purchased from one of the entomological suppliers. If the species happens to be a rare immigrant, it can be argued that to release bred adults might give a false picture of their occurrence here. But there is a more serious objection still, which involves truly resident, perhaps locally distributed, species. Disparate colonies of butterflies and moths tend to evolve small genetic differences peculiar to themselves, and a mixture with stock from another area might introduce a weakness which could be lethal to them. This even applies to species relatively if locally common.

One needs, then, to be careful about introducing bred stock into the wild; careful but not totally inhibited. Basically, it is a matter of weighing up all the considerations with reference to the particular species concerned. Something the amateur could do is to experiment by rearing and releasing attractive and harmless species which have disappeared from certain areas as a direct result of human activity—perhaps a mixture of over-collecting or land development—or for reasons unknown. There are many examples one can think of. One is the attractive Large Tortoiseshell butterfly (*Nymphalis polychloros*), which has become steadily rarer in recent years and seems likely to be further reduced because of the depletion of its elm food-plant by Dutch elm disease. Always provided a colony does not exist in the area already, and careful investigation will reveal whether this is so, there can surely be no reason why stock (obtainable from entomological suppliers) could not be released on healthy elms at the edges of woods, along roadsides, or even in the garden. The larva is also said to feed on other trees, including fruit trees such as cherry.

With our attractive insect fauna dwindling year by year, from causes both natural (for example climatic changes) and artificial, many more attempts at reintroduction could and should be made. Even should the exercise prove a failure, it is surely better than dooming all one's insect livestock to the setting-board. There may, after all, come a time when insects are considered as attractive to study in the field as birds—and few now would think of putting *them* in a glass case.

The Adonis Blue butterfly (*Lysandra bellargus*): a local species confined to chalk and limestone areas of southern England. The upper surfaces of the male's wings are a superb bright blue, whereas the female is much darker and duller. *(G. E. Hyde)*

9

RARE AND BEAUTIFUL

One of the first things the entomologist is likely to be asked when called upon to identify or give his views about an insect is whether or not it is rare. If, as is probable, the enquirer is told his find is quite common, he is generally disappointed and quickly loses interest; or perhaps he feels vaguely cheated. After all, he (or she) has never seen one before, so surely it must be uncommon? The fact is simply that the average person usually notices only the more active and conspicuous insects.

To describe any insect—indeed, any *thing*—as rare is somehow to add to its appeal. An obsession with rarities has long been a feature of popular natural history study. The amateur bird-watcher, compiling his 'tick-list', feels his day has been made if he can add one or two rare vagrants to his quota. This is at least better than shooting them for taxidermy or collecting their eggs, as used to be the fashion; but it is really of no more value than the schoolboy train-spotter's craze for filling his notebook with numbers. The situation is much worse in entomology because here the subjects *are* collected, and again the emphasis is all too often upon the rarity. Whether collecting has, by itself, reduced certain species to rarity or extinguished others is difficult to assess, for other factors are also involved, such as the vagaries of our climate, the destruction of habitats, and the fact that many species in Britain are at the fringe of their natural distribution anyway; but certainly it must have hastened the decline of many insect species—species which have probably never been common in Britain at any time and are therefore all the more attractive to the man with a net.

Advising tyro entomologists on the pros and cons of collecting is not easy; many insect groups are difficult or even impossible to identify without the closest examination, sometimes even dissection, and precise determination of species must always be the serious student's aim; but by and large, 'collecting' today is better done with notebook, camera and pencil, for both ethical and practical reasons. From the purely aesthetic point of view, no insect ever looks the same dead and set as it does when vibrant with life and in its natural surroundings: a collection of insects, however beautifully laid out, is a sad thing by comparison.

While never having possessed that inner compulsion to preserve elusive beauty, I can nevertheless share with all entomologists a quickening of the pulse on encountering some extraordinarily rare species. My own first sighting of *Cicadetta montana*, described in Chapter 4, was an undoubted highlight in my entomological life, as was the opportunity to rear the caterpillar of a Death's Head hawk-moth when it was given to me after having narrowly escaped destruction under the heel of an irate potato grower. Moreover, there is always the opportunity of 'cheating' by going abroad to see species which are rare in Britain, but commoner elsewhere. I shall never forget my first sighting of a Camberwell Beauty butterfly (*Nymphalis antiopa*) in North Poland a good many years ago, for here is a species which is indeed both rare and beautiful, with those great plum-coloured wings edged with splashes of bright blue and an outer frill of palest yellow. There, too, I saw a Large Copper butterfly (*Lycaena dispar*), which is now extinct as a truly wild species in Britain, although attempts have been made, with only moderate success, to introduce the Dutch sub-species *batavus* at Woodwalton Fen in East Anglia.

One of Britain's rarest butterflies: the Black Hairstreak (*Strymonidia pruni*), a male, sampling privet flowers. This species is a resident in Britain but is now apparently confined to a few localities in the midlands. *(G. E. Hyde)*

Camberwell Beauty butterfly (*Nymphalis antiopa*). Enlarged × 1½ approx.

The Camberwell Beauty is one of several butterflies which are afforded British status on the strength of their regular appearance here as immigrants, mainly from Northern Europe. It has apparently never been known to breed in Britain, mainly because even if the adults survive our winters they have little or no chance of meeting a mate. Occasionally, however, the species arrives in such numbers as to increase the possibility of producing a truly British succession. In 1976, the best year for more than a century, scores of reports came in from as far afield as Kent, the Isle of

98

Man and northernmost Scotland. One of them turned up a few miles from my home, but of course I missed it and did not see another.

That other famous insect immigrant from the Continent, the Death's Head hawk-moth, finds it equally difficult to establish itself here, but for slightly different reasons. It breeds all right; almost every year hundreds of caterpillars and pupae turn up on potato plots throughout the length and breadth of Britain. But unfortunately few, if any, survive our winters unless they are taken indoors and 'forced'. Unlike the Camberwell Beauty, which on arrival here in late summer and autumn, generally spends only a short time on the wing before going into hibernation, the female Death's Heads have previously mated and carry fertile eggs. These they deposit, usually singly, on cultivated potato leaves, as well as occasionally on nightshades, thorn-apple, tea-tree (*Lycium*), and some other plants. Presumably the moths die shortly after, or are snapped up by collectors. Their progeny reach the pupal stage in autumn but fail to produce moths the following spring because, again, they do not survive our cold, wet winters.

The likelihood of finding the caterpillars or the subterranean pupae of this impressive moth is somewhat slim, but perhaps less so than one might imagine. An entomologist friend tells me that some years ago a Boston man advertised in his local paper for *atropos* pupae, offering 2s 6d (12½p) each. Over seventy were subsequently sent to him! One doubts if he was long out of pocket, either, for if he kept them carefully in captivity, even a few of the emerged moths could have made him a handsome profit if sold to collectors or dealers. Nor in this case could one have blamed him, for the insects would not have survived if released. On the other hand, with that number of pupae there would surely be a good proportion of both males and females, which might have been induced to mate in captivity.

If the reasons for the rarity of immigrants such as these are fairly clear, it is much less easy to explain the parlous state of some of our resident species. I know, for example, of a locality where the Black Hairstreak (*Strymonidia pruni*)—one of our very rarest butterflies—is as common on warm, sunny days in May and June as cabbage whites fluttering about a brassica patch. And yet there are probably no more than a handful of such colonies in the whole of Britain, confined so far as we know to a few midland counties. Its food-plant, blackthorn or sloe, is common enough, despite some depletion of hedges, so its rarity is something of a mystery. It seems unlikely that collecting can be the primary cause.

The Black Hairstreak is likely to be a disappointment to those who expect a rarity to be of striking appearance. The species is attractive enough in its way—blackish-brown hind wings checkered on the upper and lower borders with orange—but certainly nothing spectacular. The ubiquitous Small Tortoisehell (*Aglais urticae*), which nearly everybody knows, far outshines it in beauty of colours and pattern.

Perhaps this is a significant point, for it is surely true to say that *all* insects are beautiful, in their way, common or rare—even

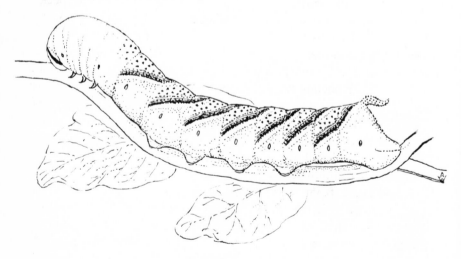

Caterpillar of Death's Head Hawk-moth (*Acherontia atropos*). About actual size.

the universally loathed House fly, the Cockroach and the Earwig! Perhaps these require something of the eye of faith to appreciate fully, but with butterflies like the Small Tortoiseshell, Peacock and Brimstone, it is often a case of familiarity breeding contempt. We see but do not regard them; we take them for granted. And yet apart from their beauty species like these would well repay further study. What flowers do they and other common garden species prefer to visit, for example, and what *coloured* flowers, linked to scent? Butterflies such as these are often seen with their wings damaged by bird beaks. Did they escape because they tasted unpleasant, and how often do their cryptic-cum-warning-colour defences fail to work? Indeed, how many times has predation by birds and other animals been observed on these butterflies? Studies of this kind are open to any patient amateur observer, and this says nothing of the myriads of common smaller and less spectacular insects, many of which have received scarcely any attention from the spare-time entomologist.

The best naturalists have always been those who devoted their attention to the commonest and most easily discovered species. Gilbert White's list of rarities during many years of studying the wildlife in his parish of Selborne was relatively short; yet he is now rightly considered one of the pioneers of field natural history, simply because by studying the commonest animals and plants and other natural phenomena in depth, he added considerably to our knowledge. The same applies even more appositely to the great French entomologist Jean Henri Fabre, whose *Souvenirs Entomologiques* convey a salutary lesson to anyone studying insects that the most wonderful discoveries can be made with the familiar species found almost literally on one's doorstep.

Quite apart from their status as serious naturalists, I like to think that men such as these shared my aesthetic view of insects as a whole—that 'rare and beautiful' can be applied as much to the very commonest and sometimes most uninteresting-looking animals and plants, including insects, as to the most elusive ones. This is using 'rare' in the Oxford Dictionary sense of having

Close-up view of a hornets' nest, enlarged by about two-thirds. Hornets (*Vespa crabro*) are less aggressive than is popularly imagined and will not usually attack man unless their nest is interfered with.　　*(Robin Fletcher)*

'uncommon excellence' and because our knowledge of such species despite their commonness is often far less than we imagine. 'Beautiful' requires no elaboration in the more colourful or attractively patterned species; but how many people look twice at the intricate patterning on a moth's forewings, perhaps designed for cryptic camouflage, or the superb bronze sheen of a leaf-beetle's elytra? How many use a magnifying glass to see the marvellous way an insect's legs articulate or how its compound eyes are made up of a myriad separate facets? The recent advances in colour photography, and the publication of books containing close-up shots of insects have done much to bring these phenomena to popular notice, but do they encourage people to go out and look at insects for themselves? Possibly the effect is quite the reverse, in implying that there is nothing that has not been studied, nothing that has not been photographed; that because these things have been published there is nothing more to learn.

But these and a myriad other marvellous living things are all around us, full of surprises for the patient observer. It is of course right to be concerned about the status of rare species, but popular support for endangered insects will only come I feel when more people appreciate that the very commonest of them are worth looking at and cherishing too. Even common insects may not always remain so. Nowadays, for example, familiar butterflies like Small Tortoiseshell and Peacock, as well as immigrant Red Admiral and Painted Lady, are finding life increasingly difficult as the nettles they feed on are ruthlessly sprayed out of existence. Does any item —butterfly or beetle, painting or porcelain—have to become scarce before it is properly appreciated? This certainly seems to apply to art, often with scant reference to technical excellence. An essential difference between paintings and butterflies is that the former can always be duplicated. Animals, once extinguished, cannot.

Forewing of Buff Arches moth (*Habrosyne pyritoides*). Enlarged × 1½ approx.

Small Magpie moth (*Eurrhypara hortilata*). Actual size.

10

WHAT'S IN A NAME?

It doesn't take an entomologist long to realise that it is one thing to find insects, but quite another to name them. Problems of identification arise at every turn, because of the sheer numbers involved and the close similarity between many species. The whole issue is complicated by the fact that insects have the frustrating habit of producing offspring totally unlike themselves, both in shape and colour, or lacking adult characters in other ways. Even seasoned entomologists may find themselves baffled, or driven to express their opinions in evasive or vague terms when asked to determine a species—particularly if it is dead, for many insects quickly deteriorate after death.

It is partly for such reasons, too, that professional and museum entomologists (and many amateurs) tend to specialise in just one or two Orders, like dragonflies or grasshoppers, or even in one family such as the vast *Staphylinidae* or rove-beetle family which alone comprises some 1,000 of the 3,700 or so species of beetles known to occur in Britain. Specialisation is even more necessary in warmer countries where the insect populations are correspondingly larger.

Another complication—even irritation—the novice encounters at the outset lies in the fact that our more familiar species have two quite distinct types of names—common or everyday ones (often called 'popular' names), and scientific double-barrelled efforts. Examples are the Two-spot Ladybird which scientists call *Coccinella bipunctata* and the Large White butterfly, *Pieris brassicae.* If one browses through certain of the entomological journals one will find heated controversy about whether the student should use scientific names alone, or both scientific and popular ones. No one seriously suggests there is any sense in using *just* the common ones, despite the fact that most entomologists are amateurs. Common, or folk, names for insects are often extremely picturesque, attractive and descriptive, but by their very nature they are intended for use only in the country where they were coined. Since entomological science, and zoology in general, is international, it would be extremely confusing for an entomologist from one country to correspond with a colleague in another in purely colloquial terms; often, neither would know what the other was talking about.

Such difficulties are more likely to arise in communication between entomologists whose native language is different; but misunderstandings also occur in English-speaking countries. 'Glow-worm,' for example, is wildly inaccurate zoologically, because the species is an insect and not a worm. Among fellow countrymen this presents few problems. But then we find that in New Zealand 'glow-worm' is the name for a quite different insect: the larva of a Mycetophilid (Dipterid, or two-winged) fly, with the scientific name

Seven-spot ladybird (*Coccinella septempunctata*) preying on greenfly. Lady-birds kill and eat aphides and scale-insects, which are injurious to cultivated plants, in both adult and larval stages, but often have to contend with ants which milk the aphides for their honey-dew but do not harm them.

(*Robin Fletcher*)

of *Arachnocampa luminosa*, which lives in dark bush country and the depths of caves like that at Waitomo on North Island. This in fact provides a splendid argument in favour of scientific names and classification because it once led to a curious and highly revealing misunderstanding of the kind I have mentioned. Aware of my interest in the European glow-worm, the estate agent managing the publicity interests of certain West Country caves wrote asking my advice as to the feasibility of introducing glow-worms into the caves as an added attraction for visitors. Of course, I had to disillusion him because our *Lampyris noctiluca* is adapted to outdoor conditions and a fairly high ambient temperature that would make it impossible for it to survive or glow in the cool depths of a cave. As I suspected, my correspondent was confusing our British glow-worm with its Antipodean namesake. Had he been an entomologist, perhaps, the misunderstanding might never have arisen, and I would not have been provided with such a splendidly apposite anecdote!

There are many other instances where confusion can arise with the sole use of common names. If you write to an American about the daddy long-legs you see dancing up and down your windows, he might well be puzzled because to him daddy long-legs don't have wings and are usually confined to ground level. The difficulty resolves itself when one realises that in America the colloquialism is applied to harvestmen, eight-legged relatives of spiders, which we commonly find lurking in undergrowth or beneath old sacks, etc: they are not insects at all. *Our* daddy long-legs is the crane-fly, whose larvae are the fat grey leatherjackets that make nasty bare brown patches on your lawn.

Many people use the term 'bug' for practically any small creeping invertebrate animal—not just insects, but even micro-organisms like bacteria! But entomologically it has a most specific application only to the Hemiptera, all of which are characterized by the possession of piercing, sucking mouthparts. The historic use of 'fly', whether by itself or as a suffix (e.g. ichneumon-fly, caddis-fly, dragonfly) is also misleading, since the only true flies are those insects belonging to the order Diptera, or two-winged insects, such as the common house fly. However, the epithet probably derives from the obvious point that all insects referred to in this way have wings; that is, can *fly*.

For reasons like these, then, entomologists, and indeed all serious naturalists, employ what they at least intend shall be a standard system of naming, designed to be understood by students as far afield as London and Lima. Each species has two names, a generic and a specific one. In the case of the Large White, this is *Pieris brassicae*. *Pieris* is the genus, which includes several other similar and closely related species (e.g. *Pieris rapae*, the Small White, *Pieris napi*, Green-veined White), and *brassicae* the species. Sometimes there is a slight departure from this rule in that a further name may be added to indicate a local race or variety of the species, such as *Papilio machaon britannicus*, for the British sub-species of the Swallowtail butterfly. The scientific name is followed (at least in technical scientific parlance) by the name of the authority (often abbreviated) who first gave the insect its scientific name—for example, "L." or "Linn." for Linnaeus, the great 18th-century Swedish naturalist who invented the system.

Binomial nomenclature, being a highly artificial system, has its imperfections. Frequently, for example, the same species is given different names, quite independently and unknowingly, by different workers. When this happens the first—that is, the oldest—name must in general be adopted under what are known as the Rules of Priority, although this doesn't stop the superseded name from being used as a synonym. Apart from this, systematists are continually re-organising and rearranging the nomenclature of insects and other animals, according to new ideas and opinions of relationships, so that there is much less permanency in scientific names than one might imagine. It is probably true to say that all this chopping and changing causes as much confusion as the use of solely colloquial names referred to earlier.

This can be seen in the entomological magazines, where a passage of descriptive text may be so littered with double- or ɪriple-barrelled names, naming authorities, synonyms, and so on, as to make extremely tedious reading. Perhaps the only answer in such situations is to list all the species' common names and scientific equivalents at the end of the article, and give just one of them in the paper itself, preferably, if the periodical has an international circulation, the scientific ones.

It is probably worth pointing out that only a minute proportion of the world's insects are sufficiently familiar to possess common names, whereas all the known ones *do* have scientific ones.

Now, I would be the last person to suggest we discard popular

The curious snake-fly, *Raphidia maculicollis*, one of only four species occurring in Britain. These insects frequently hold their head at an angle to the elongated prothorax which, with the tapering ovipositor, gives them a snake-like appearance. Adult snake-flies are most often seen in deciduous woodlands and the larval stage is spent beneath the bark of old trees where they prey on other tiny insects and other invertebrates. Actual size almost $\frac{3}{4}$ inch.   *(J. A. Grant)*

names, even within the hallowed pages of the specialist literature. Indeed, I am very much their champion, if only because they bring animal study down to a level that everyone, scientist and layman, can understand. This apart, such names are, I have always felt, a part of our heritage: composites of traditional and individual entomologists' ideas, local beliefs and folklore, whose origins have commonly been lost in the mist of time, and often prompt the most delightful speculation.

Some of them are picturesque in the extreme, though they often present, like the 'glow-worm' mentioned earlier, a distorted and inaccurate idea of the insects' true nature. In many parts of Britain, for example, the larger dragonflies of the 'darter' and 'hawker' type—those with long, thin pointed bodies—are called 'devil's darning-needles' or 'horse-stingers'. The former is pure folklorish whimsy, of course, but the latter is of even more interest because it perpetuates a belief, still current today, that these impressive 'flying dragons' attack and sting not merely horses but ourselves too. The uninitiated is often nervous when a large dragon-fly flits by his ear or even, as sometimes happens if he is wearing bright clothing, rests on his clothes or person (the insects have excellent vision and probably good colour perception). There is no substance in the horse-stinging idea, although one can think of reasons how and why it arose. Quietly grazing near a river or lake, horses commonly attract clouds of flies. Now, dragonflies are confirmed predators, both as adults and nymphs, and the former are adept at catching their prey in full flight. What more logical, then, that a dragonfly should see the flies buzzing about a horse's head as a concentration of its prey and zoom in to take advantage of it? What more natural, too, that a human observer, unaware of the true story behind the picture, should assume that the dragonfly was attacking the horse, particularly since Dobbin himself might not always have taken kindly to the insect's proximity and tossed its head in irritation. The very name 'dragonfly' has an appropriate imagery all its own. If there were such things as flying dragons, they would be hard put to match the dragonfly's supreme mastery of flight, able as it is to turn, tack and hover or even fly backwards at will and at a great rate.

Delving into the etymology of everyday names for insect groups or individual species is a fascinating exercise in itself. In fact, it really deserves a book all to itself. 'Cricket', for example, derives from the old French verb *criquer*, to creak, and 'beetle' from the Old English *bitula*, a biter. 'Chafer' (a type of beetle) comes from the German for beetle, *käfer*, and has a connotation of gnawing or chewing. Many of them are pretty accurate and descriptive in their way, whereas others, like 'earwig', are not. The belief that these insects enter the ear and even pierce the eardrum is surprisingly widespread. Many stories are told of horrors perpetrated by these much misunderstood creatures. Oscar Cook in his short story *Boomerang*, for example, tells of a giant Bornean earwig which was introduced into the ear of a man by a jealous rival and

Young caterpillar of a Puss moth (*Cerura vinula*). Enlarged × 3 approx. Shows the curious dorsal markings, reminiscent of a caricature of a cat viewed from the rear.

110

proceeded to bore right through and out the other one—but not before, horror upon horror, depositing her eggs in his brain! Such fancies seem current outside fiction. An old lady who was once my neighbour told me a similar story of a deranged girl whose brain pan was found to be teeming with earwigs after death. I know of no medical precedent to account for ideas of this sort, and the recent discovery of a snippet of information in an old magazine makes me wonder if the superstition is the result of a misunderstanding. In France, for example, earwigs are commonly called *perce-oreille*, or 'ear-piercer'—but not in any horrific sense. The writer of the note in question considered that the epithet derived from the resemblance of the male earwig's pincers to the tool which Parisian jewellers once used (and perhaps still do) to pierce the ear lobes for the attachment of earrings. He illustrated a pair of these pincers and I must say the similarity provides a highly convincing explanation of the whole curious matter.

In no group of insects is there such a plethora of common names —names weird and wonderful, outlandish and fanciful—like those used for moths. There are Emperors, Footmen and Lackeys, Heralds, Swords and Daggers, as well as a host of species named after various mammals and birds because of some resemblance, fancied or real, to these creatures, either in the adult or larval stages. Thus we have Sharks and Tigers, Hawks and Lobster, Elephant Hawk and Fox, as well as the Puss and Kittens mentioned in earlier chapters. Hawk-moths are so-called because of the efficient sharp-winged flight of these masters of the air, Lobster because its caterpillar has a curious extension of the abdomen very like the pincers of these crustaceans. The Elephant-hawk is so-named because of the tapering trunk-like extension of the larva's head end, while the Fox moth presumably derives its title from the russet coloration of both moth and hirsute caterpillar. The Puss moth, and its relatives the Kittens, have long been of particular interest to me since it is a moot point whether their names derive from the fluffy moths themselves, which admittedly remind one of pussy willow catkins, or the curiously marked caterpillars.

111

The latter have twin terminal tails, which are commonly held close together, plus a pair of large dark tubercles on each side of the head, and these features together with the peculiar dorsal markings against a lighter background present an unmistakable likeness to a Felix-like caricature of a domestic cat seated on its haunches with its back to the viewer. Another of my favourite moth names is Mouse: highly apposite and descriptive for the species has a habit of running rapidly over the ground in a scuttling mouse-like manner, and has the same indeterminate greyish colour.

Some moth names bestir the imagination in a most delightful way. The Mother Shipton, for example, was so called (we are told) because the patterning on the moth's forewings is supposed to resemble that ancient personage's profile; and indeed if one looks sideways at each wing one can clearly make out the hooked nose, evil-looking eye and upturned chin of this supposed witch. The Old Lady moth itself conveys a slightly different picture; the subtly patterned wings of this large moth prompt comparison with an old lady clad in a dark shawl. A correspondent of mine once wrote amusingly of seeing an Old Lady moth *on* a tea-house, evoking a truly splendid mental image of human eccentricity!

Many people find it difficult to distinguish larger moths such as these from butterflies, and I am reminded of the woman who exclaimed 'What a beautiful butterfly!' when I pointed out a fine Engrailed moth at rest in the bus shelter we were occupying. However, her remark was understandable since the differences between moths and butterflies are far from clear cut, and in any case it was by no means as wide of the mark as some I have heard. I have known Wasp-beetles suspected of being Colorado beetles or even, incredible as it sounds, gnat larvae taken to be tadpoles— and that from a gardener! The Wasp-beetle's aping of its stinging model has been referred to elsewhere; 'Colorado' beetle reminds one that this much-travelled species is not native to Britain and Europe at all, but is American in origin. Other beetle colloquialisms are revealing in a different way. 'Dor' beetle, for example, seems to be an allusion to the loud droning sound the insect makes in

112

Three views of the butterfly-like Swallowtailed moth (*Ourapteryx sambu-caria*). Almost actual size.

flight, reminiscent of a sleeper's snore. The Devil's Coach-horse derives its splendid epithet from a mediæval legend that the devil uses its body to hide in; when it turns up its tail—hence 'cocktail', its alternative name—it is supposed to be pronouncing a curse.

The names of several of our native insects, notably butterflies, derive their origins from the classical languages, Latin and Greek, and some are called after characters in Greek and Latin mythology. 'Fritillary' derives from the Latin *fritillus*, a dice-box, in reference to the spotted and checkered pattern of these butterflies' wings. 'Adonis' blue is an obvious allusion to the handsome youth whom Venus vainly sought to charm, while the epithet 'argus', applied to several of our butterflies, refers to the hundred-eyed giant of that name. The argus butterflies have eye-like patterns on the upper and lower sides of their wings. Most scientific names are derived from Greek or Latin, and some have a splendid roll to them—like *Acherontia atropos*, for the great Death's Head hawk-moth, which has already been mentioned more than once. Acheron was a river in Hades, while Atropos was one of the three Fates—which seems as good a point as any at which to end this chapter and give way to the serious business of insect classification in the next.

11

ORDER OUT OF CHAOS

How Insects are Classified

Like all animals, insects must have had a common ancestor way back in their evolutionary history: perhaps something similar to the primitive *Diplura*, or two-pronged bristletails, which appear to provide a link with centipedes. Over many millions of years, however, insects have diverged enormously, though still retaining the same general structure, displaying greater or lesser affinities with each other. It is on this basis of structural affinity, both larval and adult, that entomologists sub-divide the great Class *Insecta* (which includes all the world's known insects) into different Orders. The actual number of Orders depends on which authority you recognise, for there is much difference of opinion between them. Some, for example, regard the alder-flies, lacewings and snake-flies as sufficiently different to justify separate ordinal status; others group them together in one Order, the *Neuroptera*. The following list is a fairly conservative one; it is not entirely scientific since I have arranged and described the Orders roughly in order of conspicuousness and familiarity rather than on grounds of relationship between them. The number of species given is in many cases only approximate.

Butterflies and Moths *(Lepidoptera: Greek* lepidos, *a scale,* pteron, *a wing) 2,200 British species; 150,000 world.*

The differences between butterflies and moths are so subtle that it is scarcely surprising many people describe one as the other. In Britain, conveniently, all of the 68 species of butterflies (many of them rare or uncertain immigrants) are day-fliers, but there are many moths which fly by day too. The main physical difference is that the antennae of butterflies end in a distinct, drumstick-like club, whereas those of moths are variously simple and thread-like, feathered or barbed, or ending in a hook. Butterflies hold their wings together in flight by means of a simple fold device, while moths employ a bristle-and-hook method. There are, however, exceptions to the rule, notably in the case of the Swift moths which employ the butterflies' technique of ensuring that the two pairs of wings operate in unison.

Dragonflies *(Odonata:* odontos, *a tooth) 46 British species; 5000 world.*

The scientific name of this group refers to the strong mandibles of the adults, which are equally as predacious as their aquatic nymphs. The adult insects also have very large compound eyes, taking up the greater part of the head region, but very short antennae. The Odonata are further sub-divided into two distinct groups: the *Anisoptera*, or typical dragonflies, which usually hold their wings laterally when at rest; and the *Zygoptera*, or damsel-flies (also called demoiselles) which generally hold them together vertically. The latter are also smaller and more delicately built. Mating is a peculiar affair in dragonflies, the male (who is often very differently coloured from the female) grasping his partner's neck by means of his tail claspers, while the female arches her own abdomen until it touches the male's second abdominal segment wherein lies his pairing organ. It is often possible to see dragonflies and damsel-flies flying about thus in tandem.

Beetles *(Coleoptera:* coleos, *a sheath;* pteron, *a wing) 3700 British species; 300,000 world.*

Most numerous in species of all the insect orders, beetles typically

115

have their forewings hardened and strengthened with chitin as a means of protecting the lower pair, although some species and the females of others (e.g. the glow-worm) are wingless. Beetles vary enormously in size, from several inches down to a millimetre or so, and also in their habits, food and habitats. They exist on land and water and may be carnivorous, vegetarian, omnivorous or scavenging. Quite frequently, the larval diet is very different from that of the adults, some of which scarcely feed at all. Some of the better known groups of beetles are the stag, ground and rove beetles, ladybirds, weevils, longhorns, chafers, dung beetles, burying and carrion beetles, and diving beetles.

Bloody-nosed beetle (*Timarcha tenebricosa*). Enlarged × 2 approx.

Bugs *(Hemiptera:* hemi, *half;* pteron, *wing) 1630 British species; 50,000 world.*

While superficially similar to beetles in general appearance, bugs are characterised by their piercing, sucking mouthparts, whereas beetles' jaws are adapted for cutting and chewing. Careful examination will reveal this tube-like *rostrum* which when not in use is doubled back under the head like a jack-knife. Two main sub-orders of bugs are recognised. *Homoptera* (frog-hoppers, aphides, cicada, etc) either have two pairs of similar wings or the upper pair hardened for protection. *Heteroptera* (shield-bugs, capsids, pond-skaters, water-boatmen, water scorpions, etc.) have the tips of their otherwise leathery forewings membraneous, the latter overlapping at the end of the abdomen when the wings are not in use. There are as usual exceptions to the rule in the shape of groups like bed-bugs and water-measurer, which are wingless; some aphis forms are also flightless.

A Heteropterid Ground bug (unidentified). Greatly enlarged.

Bees, Wasps, Ants Etc. *(Hymenoptera:* hymen, *a membrane;* pteron, *a wing) 6200 British species; 100,000 world.*

This order includes a vast assemblage of insects of varied appearance and habits. Apart from the social bees, wasps and ants, there are plant-eating sawflies and gall-wasps and wood-boring wood-wasps, as well as predatory and parasitic groups like ichneumons, chalcids, braconids, sand-, digger- and spider-wasps, and many others. The socially organised ants, vespoid wasps and many bees have three distinct castes—queen, drones (males) and workers (sex-less females). However, most are solitary, without a caste system. Typically, Hymenopterids have two pairs of wings, but some are wingless. Worker ants never possess wings, while even the queen and drones lose theirs after mating. The sting of ants, bees and wasps is actually a modified ovipositor or egg-laying tool, which explains why males do not have one.

117

Flies *(Diptera:* di, *two;* pteron, *wing) 5200 British species; 80,000 world.*

An immediate distinction between these insects and the bees and wasps which they often mimic is that they possess only one pair of wings, whereas Hymenopterids, when they have wings, possess two pairs. In true flies, the hind pair of wings are reduced to club-like processes, called halteres, which probably act as balancers and may be seen most clearly in the well-known crane-flies or daddy long-legs. Many species, such as the house fly, feed by external digestion, spreading saliva on their food and then sucking it up through their proboscis. Others are nectar- or pollen-feeders (e.g. hover-flies), while still more, such as horse-flies, mosquitoes and certain wingless species, suck the blood of mammals and birds.

Crickets and Grasshoppers *(Orthoptera:* orthos, *straight;* pteron, *a wing) 30 British species; 10,000 world.*

As described in Chapter 4 the long-horned crickets, bush-crickets and mole-crickets make their stridulating sounds in a subtly different way from the short-horned grasshoppers. All have greatly developed hind-legs, although grasshoppers are the better acrobats; crickets, bush-crickets and mole-crickets prefer to run, walk or climb. Female crickets have distinctive, pointed ovipositors, while those of bush-crickets are often flat, curved and sabre-like. Grass-hoppers bear no such visible aids to egg-laying. While most species have their underwings protected by a horny upper pair (called *tegmina*), some are flightless or with only vestigial wings.

Cockroaches *(Dictyoptera:* dictyon, *a net;* pteron, *a wing) 9 British species; 3,500 world.*

This order is usually extended to include the praying mantids, which do not occur in Britain and number about 1800 species. Cockroaches have flattened bodies and extremely long thread-like antennae; many have long membraneous wings which fold over

118

the abdomen and lack covers; others, like the Common Cockroach (*Blatta orientalis*) of houses, are unable to fly. Some smaller species occur out of doors on low vegetation.

Earwigs *(Dermaptera:* derma, *skin;* pteron, *wing) 7 British species; 900 world.*

Most people can recognise an earwig, and even tell the male from the female, the former having more strongly curved forceps. The short, waistcoat-like wing-covers protect large membraneous wings which, in our commonest species (*Forficula auricularia*) seem to be used rarely, although others, such as the small Tawny Earwig (*Labia minor*) fly readily during the day.

Lacewings, Alder-flies and Snake-flies *(Neuroptera:* neuron, *a nerve;* pteron, *a wing) 60 British species; 4000 world.*

All of these insects are characterised by two pairs of large, distinctively veined wings. The best-known of our lacewings (*Chrysopa carnea*) has a pale green body, greenish wings, long antennae and reddish eyes; its larva is the 'aphis-lion' described in the text. Alder-flies are dark, heavy bodied insects, whose larvae are aquatic; the adults are sluggish fliers, being found mostly near ponds and lakes. They lay close-packed mats of eggs on reed fronds. Snake-flies are so-called because of their elongated thorax and head, the latter being held in such a way as to look like a cobra about to strike; their bodies are also thin, and the females bear long needle-like ovipositors which heighten the snake-like appearance.

Scorpion-flies *(Mecoptera:* mekos, *length;* pteron, *a wing) 4 British species; 300 world.*

Often to be seen resting on hedgerow vegetation, scorpion-flies have their mouth-parts curiously extended into a kind of beak; their wings are transparent, except for black markings. Their common name derives from the male, the tip of whose abdomen

119

(the genital capsule) is upcurved, reddish-orange in colour and shaped like a scorpion's sting; the female's abdomen is tapering and pointed.

May-flies *(Ephemeroptera:* ephemeros, *day-living;* pteron, *a wing)* *46 British species; 1400 world.*

Best known to anglers and aquarists, these delicate tinsel-winged insects present something of a paradox in that while the adults do indeed commonly live for only a day or so, perhaps only a few hours, the larvae take several years to reach maturity. This disparity between larval and adult life-span is a common phenomenon in the insect world, but is nowhere more extremely marked than in the may-flies. Adult may-flies have two pairs of wings, the fore pair of which are much the larger; the abdomen is commonly upcurved and bears two or three long tail filaments.

Caddis-flies *(Trichoptera:* trichos, *a hair;* pteron, *a wing) 193 British species; 3000 world.*

These insects look not unlike certain moths, except that their wings are sparsely clothed with small hairs and not scales; they also have longer antennae than most moths. Caddis larvae live on the beds of rivers and lakes within protective cases made of minute pieces of gravel, stick or even, most beautifully, of tiny shells.

Stone-flies *(Plecoptera:* plekein, *fold;* pteron, *a wing) 34 British species; 1500 world.*

The most obvious distinguishing features of these rather sluggish insects, which are almost invariably found near water, are the conspicuous pair of tail filaments and the perfectly transparent wings overlapping on the back; the antennae are long and thread-like. The larvae (nymphs) are aquatic and bear conspicuous breathing gills.

Springtails *(Collembola:* kolla, *glue;* embolon, *a peg) 304 British species; 1500 world.*

Springtails derive their common name from an ability to leap powerfully when disturbed in their hiding places such as leaf litter or under stones. They jump by means of a forked device which is thrust forcibly against the surface on which the insect is resting, thus propelling the springtail several inches into the air. Scavengers by nature, the British species are very small and dull coloured. Some have long antennae and bristly bodies, but all are wingless.

Fleas *(Siphonaptera:* siphon, *a tube;* a, *without;* pteron, *a wing) 56 British species; 1100 world.*

The lack of wings in fleas is compensated by their well-known ability to jump. All are flattened laterally and have piercing, sucking mouthparts with which they feed on the blood of mammals and birds; some species, such as the hedgehog flea, are peculiar to particular animals. Flea larvae are not unlike those of flies *(Diptera)* and feed on various waste materials.

Book-lice *(Psocoptera:* Psocos, *sand;* pteron, *a wing) 87 British species; 1000 world.*

Psocids are extremely minute insects, but with long antennae, mostly scavenging or vegetarian in habit, which are found variously in old paper, dead leaves, under bark or on vegetation, or in the nests of various animals. Some species are winged, but those living a purely sedentary existence, such as the Book-louse *Trogium pulsatorium,* commonly found in old books, are not.

Sucking-lice *(Anoplura:* anoplos, *unarmed;* oura, *a tail) 25 British species; 230 world.*

This group of lice includes those species which commonly afflict man and other mammals by sucking their blood, each species being usually peculiar to one species of mammal.

Biting-lice *(Mallophaga:* mallos, *wool;* phagos, *feeding) 514 British species; 2600 world.*

Although parasites, like the Anoplura, biting-lice do not suck blood but feed on wool, hair, skin fragments, etc. of birds and mammals. Like sucking-lice, they are wingless and have short antennae.

Three-pronged Bristletails *(Thysanura:* thysanos, *fringe;* oura, *tail) 9 British species; 400 world.*

The best-known of this flightless group is the silverfish, common in houses, although most species are found out of doors in leaf litter. All have three long tail filaments, but are thin-bodied, and none is more than about 2 cm long.

Two-pronged Bristletails *(Diplura:* diplos, *double;* oura, *tail) 12 British species; 400 world.*

As their scientific name suggests, these minute insects are distinguished from the Thysanura by the possession of two tail filaments. They also have long antennae which apparently assume the role of eyes, lacking in the Diplura. Mostly scavengers, the best-known British species, *Campodea staphylinus,* is frequently found under stones or in the nests of ants, which tolerate it as a waste-feeder. It is colourless and wingless, like all diplurans.

Thrips *(Thysanoptera:* thysanos, *a fringe;* pteron, *a wing) 160 British species; 3000 world.*

The ordinal name of this group refers to the insects' two pairs of wings which are delicately fringed with fine hairs. Most are no more than a few millimetres long and feed by sucking the tissues of various plants, though some are said to be predatory on equally small insects like aphides. The antennae are very short.

Proturans *(Protura:* protos, *simple;* oura, *tail) 11 British species; 200 world.*

Colourless insects rarely more than a millimetre long, proturans lack wings and antennae although the first pair of legs, held forward and assuming their role, look rather like feelers. These insects live in damp places, for example beneath tree bark, in the soil and under stones.

Stylops *(Strepsiptera:* strepsis, *twisting;* pteron, *a wing) 16 British species; 400 world.*

Frequently still classified among the beetles, stylops are strange, little seen insects whose larvae live as parasites in the nests of bees, wasps, ants and plant bugs. The oddly-shaped wings are present only in the male, females spending all their lives in their hosts' nests.

Note. Certain insect orders are unrepresented in Britain. They include the Embioptera (web-spinners), Phasmida (stick and leaf insects), Isoptera (termites), and Zoraptera.

SELECTED FURTHER READING

In recent years there has been something of a spate of new books on insects, many of them basically pictorial since photographers and publishers are beginning to realise just how visually effective they can be when vastly enlarged by the camera. The following list is naturally highly selective; it should not be taken too rigidly since many of the titles apply more widely than to the chapters they are listed under.

CHAPTER 1 (General entomology)

W. Blaney: *How Insects Live* (Elsevier-Phaidon 1976). A lavishly illustrated survey of insect physiology and habits, with a useful short summary of all the world's insect Orders.

A. D. Imms: *Insect Natural History* (Collins 'New Naturalist' series, revised edition 1971). Basically similar in approach to the above, but more detailed.

T. Rowland-Entwistle: *The World You Never See: Insect Life* (Hamlyn 1976). Unashamedly visual, but valuable for the magnificent colour photos produced by the famous Oxford Scientific Film Unit.

V. B. Wigglesworth: *The Life of Insects* (Weidenfeld & Nicolson 1966). Like Imms, a text rather than a 'visual experience'.

CHAPTERS 2 and 3 (Habitats)

Ake Sandhall: *Insects and Other Invertebrates in Colour* (Lutterworth 1975). Brief in treatment, but useful in that it is arranged by habitat rather than group and also covers other arthropods, such as spiders, centipedes, woodlice, etc. There is also a good classification breakdown and a valuable bibliography arranged by Orders.

Anthony Wootton: *Discovering Garden Insects and Other Invertebrates* (Shire 1975). Useful for those whose entomologizing takes them no further than the garden pond. Arranged by sub-habitats, e.g. flowers, trees, under stones, etc.

CHAPTER 4 (Insect sounds)

E. C. M. Haes: *Crickets and Grasshoppers of the British Isles* (British

Naturalists' Association 1973). A 16-page identification guide to all the British species.

D. R. Ragge: *Grasshoppers, Crickets and Cockroaches of the British Isles* (Warne 1965). A detailed survey, illustrated in colour, of all the British species, with helpful song-charts of each. An accompanying long-playing record, *Songs of the British Grasshoppers*, is also available.

P. T. Haskell: *Insect Sounds* (Witherby 1961). A general account.

G. W. Pierce: *The Songs of Insects* (Harvard University Press 1948).

Anthony Wootton: *Crickets and Grasshoppers* (Priory Press 1978).

CHAPTER 5 (Nocturnal insects)

J. D. Carthy: *Animal Navigation* (Allen & Unwin 1956). Includes a detailed account of insect light-orientation.

E. B. Ford: *Moths* (Collins 'New Naturalist' series, 1967). A scholarly account of moth habits; not an identification guide.

R. South: *The Moths of the British Isles*. 2 vols. (Warne 1961). An identification handbook to the larger species.

CHAPTER 6 (Glow-worms)

J. H. Fabre: *The Glow-worm and Other Insects* (Hodder & Stoughton 1919). Translated from the French, but retains Fabre's inimitable enthusiasm and charming style.

E. N. Harvey: *Living Light* (Princeton 1940). A learned account of bioluminescence generally.

V. B. Wigglesworth: 'The Light of Glow-worms and Fireflies', in *Science News* (Penguin) 12: 1940. A short account of the nature of animal light-production.

CHAPTER 7 (Insects in the house)

J. R. Busvine: *Insects and Hygiene* (Methuen 1966). The biology and control of household and medical pests of all kinds.

G. Ordish: *The Living House* (Rupert Hart-Davis 1960). The insects and other animals that live in a 400-year old Kentish farmhouse.

CHAPTER 8 (Keeping insects)

R. L. E. Ford: *Studying Insects* (Warne 1973). Emphasis on collecting, but with useful advice on keeping and rearing butterflies and moths, bees, wasps, ants, and other groups.

H. Oldroyd: *Collecting, Preserving and Studying Insects* (Hutchinson 1970). A detailed compendium, with notes on the mechanics of classification and the writing up of observations.

M. W. F. Tweedie: *Pleasure from Insects* (David & Charles 1968). Includes a good account of keeping and photographing insects, but with a much wider application.

CHAPTER 9 (Rarities and aesthetics)

D. L. Hawksworth (Ed.): *The Changing Flora and Fauna of Britain* (Academic Press 1974). Includes discussions of threatened and declining species of some of the major insect Orders.

W. Linsenmaier: *Insects of the World* (McGraw-Hill 1972). Superb colour paintings and photos of world species.

V. J. Stanek: *The Pictorial Encyclopedia of Insects* (Hamlyn 1969). Nearly a thousand colour and black-and-white photos give a good idea of the diversity and beauty of the insect world, from the very smallest species upwards.

CHAPTERS 10 and 11 (Names and identification)

J. Burton (Ed.): *The Oxford Book of Insects* (Oxford University Press 1968). Highly selective, but a useful colour guide to the commoner species and groups.

M. Chinery: *A Field Guide to the Insects of Britain and Northern Europe* (Collins 1973). An excellent account of all the European Orders, but not of course all species, with keys, an excellent bibliography, and very fine colour paintings.

A. W. Leftwich: *A Dictionary of Entomology* (Constable 1976). Contains inaccuracies, but useful for checking up on the scientific and popular name equivalents; no etymology.

Stephen Potter and Laurens Sargent: *Pedigree: Words from Nature* (Collins 'New Naturalist' 1973). An absorbing study of the origins of everyday animal and plant names in general, with many references to those of insects.

R. D. Macleod: *Key to the Names of British Butterflies and Moths* (Pitman 1959). An excellent dictionary-type study of the classical origins of scientific names of our most popular insects, including 'micro' moths.

INDEX

Numbers in italics indicate illustrations.

INDEX